PLANTS
OF
HAWAII

how to grow them

by FORTUNATO TEHO

Revised Edition
Copyright 1992
by Fortunato Teho

1st Printing - July 1992
2nd Printing - July 1993
3rd Printing - May 1995
4th Printing - April 1997
5th Printing - July 1999

Illustrations by
Sean G. Kimura

Published in the U.S.A. by the
PETROGLYPH PRESS, LTD.
160 Kamehameha Avenue • Hilo, Hawai'i 96720
Phone 808-935-6006 / Fax 808-935-1553
reedbook@interpac.net
www.basicallybooks.com

ISBN 0-912180-48-X

TABLE OF CONTENTS

PUBLISHER'S NOTE

The information contained here was first compiled in the early 1960's. Efforts have been made to revise this latest edition to include new information on pests and diseases, especially those affecting Anthuriums and Bananas.

Suggested pest control practices have also been revised to reflect current recommendations. The suggestion of pest control chemicals and the use of trade names does not constitute an endorsement of these products by the publisher. Pesticide regulations change frequently as new information is gained, so the reader is cautioned to use the least toxic methods wherever possible, to read the label carefully and follow the instructions. The user is responsible for proper use and application of pesticides as well as storage and disposal. Consult the Cooperative Extension Service or Department of Agriculture personnel for authorized special local need registration or additional information.

Readers are encouraged to consider the health and well-being of their families, neighbors, the local ecosystem and the planet when deciding on the use of chemicals.

We are endebted to Mark Crowell and Alvin Oyadomari of Brewer Environmental Industries and Deborah Ward of the U.H. Cooperative Extension Service for suggestions on revisions and current information.

ANTHURIUM

Native to Central America, the Anthurium, a perennial, includes some 500 species of which there are climbing and herbaceous forms.

Anthurium andraeanum, which was introduced to Hawaii by way of London in 1889, is related to all species commercially cultivated in the Islands. It is a herbaceous form with clustered long-stemmed, heart shaped spadix and spathe, is long-lasting, and popular as a cut flower.

The crown of the Anthurium is composed of whorls of leaf petioles and occasional flower stalks found in the axils of the petiole. A fleshy root extends from the base of each leaf petiole that develops fine feeder roots upon contact with the growing media. Since the crown elongates as new leaves form, roots eventually have difficulty in establishing themselves. The aerial roots harden and stop growing if they do not come in contact with the growing media. Thus, it is important that media are replenished periodically so as some of it is always within reach of the growing roots.

When plants have become too tall, it may be advisable to cut them back and replant. This may be a period of about three years, depending on where and how they are grown.

Anthurium may be planted in rows, in cans or pots in the lathhouse or under a tree. Row planted Anthurium need to be cut back less often than those grown in containers.

PROPAGATION

The Anthurium may be propagated by seed, shoots or root cuttings. Seeds form on the spadix and appear as warty, berry-like swellings that may take about eight months to ripen.

Ripe seeds gathered from the spadix should be planted in a germination flat containing a clean, moist media. The seedlings should be left in the flat until they are large enough for transplanting into individual pots. After the seedlings have grown to good size, they may be transferred to larger containers or planted in the lathhouse. Plants grown in this manner are not necessarily like the mother plant and are the hybrids from which superior plants may be selected.

Shoots should never be removed from the mother plant until they have developed several roots. After the shoots are separated, a few of the older leaves should be pruned off to lessen transpiration and transplanted to containers or their permanent location. Keep the plants moist but not waterlogged.

Mature plants with long root stems may also be used to propagate new plants. The tip or crown cutting should have at least three nodes with a good root system. The balance of the root stem may be divided into cuttings of three nodes each. The root cuttings may be planted under shade in moist media to develop shoots. Allow the shoot to grow several leaves before transplanting.

WHERE AND IN WHAT TO GROW

The Anthurium does best under shade with humidity conditions that parallel its natural habitat. It will thrive in a variety of growing media that has good drainage. The features that should be considered in media selection are availability, cost, and effect on plant growth and yield. Among the types of media used to grow Anthurium are: taro peel, tree fern fiber, macadamia nut shells, coffee parchment, bagasse, leaf mold, wood shavings, soil and black sand or their combinations.

Taro peel, a waste product of poi manufacture, is the skin peelings of taro *(Colocasia esculenta)*. Tree fern fiber, derived from the tree fern *(Cibotium chamissoi)*, is available as trunks and chunks to shredded fiber. Macadamia nut shells are the hard outer coverings that protect macadamia nut kernels. Coffee parchment, a waste product of the coffee industry, is the hard skin that encloses the coffee seed.

Bagasse, a by-product of the sugar industry, is crushed sugar cane fiber after the juice has been extracted. Leaf mold is the decomposed leaves of plants and trees. Wood shavings, a waste product of planing mills, are the shavings from construction lumber. Black sand is derived from volcanic cinders.

In one replicated test growing Anthurium in the different media at the University of Hawaii, coffee parchment gave the best performance in number, size, and stem length of flowers. The others ranked in this order: bagasse, macadamia nut shells, leaf mold, taro peel, wood shavings, soil, black sand and tree fern fiber.

In another test using media combinations, wood shavings plus chicken manure produced the best results. Other combinations were ranked in this order: wood shavings and soil; black sand and tree fern fiber, used orchid media; wood shavings, tree fern fiber, used orchid media; wood shavings, tree fern fiber and chicken manure; soil and tree fern fiber.

One test combined the common media, wood shavings, with cow manure at the rate of 5 to 1. This test showed that the combination produced the highest yield of flowers at a shade level of 67 and 75 percent. Other combinations gave flower production in this order: wood shavings and soil 1 to 1, wood shavings alone, wood shavings and soil, 3 to 1 and wood shavings and soil, 5 to 1.

Tree fern fiber by itself ranked almost as well as wood shavings alone. Wood shavings and soil mixed at 1 to 1 and tree fern fiber alone ranked next best.

Bagasse, a material commonly found in sugar plantation communities, is also a good media for Anthurium culture. However, Anthuriums grown in this media, whether fresh or aged, needed to be fertilized at least once a month to give good flower production. For this purpose, use Anthurium fertilizer (6N, 14P, 7.5K, 8.7CaO).

Unpruned plants give the best performance in yield of the most satisfactory flowers. Since pruning of foliage affects stem length and size of flowers, a plant should not have less than six leaves if it is to give maximum production.

Anthurium cannot grow well under light of high intensity. Production of large flowers with long stems is best under a shade level of 75 per cent. Flower production increases under conditions of high light intensity or light shade but blossoms are of poor quality.

PEST CONTROL

For pest control, use a combination insecticide-fungicide spray. To the mixture, add a foliar fertilizer so plants can be fed in the same operation. The mixture will control both chewing and sucking insects and fungus disease. Spray once a month for best control.

Anthurium bacterial blight is a problem plaguing growers in Hawaii. Due to the nature of the disease, complete sanitation in propagation practices and culture is essential. Infected plants should be removed immediately. The U.H. Cooperative Extension Service has literature available on this subject.

Early morning or late afternoon is the best time for gathering Anthurium flowers. The flowers are of the right maturity for picking three weeks after opening or when half the spadix is white. The flowers should be cut at a slant with a sharp instrument and immediately immersed in water. A blunt instrument will plug up the channels through which water travels through the stem. Change water and cut tips regularly to prolong flower life.

AVOCADO

The Avocado or Alligator Pear *(Persea americana)* is native to the forests of tropical America and was introduced to Hawaii sometime before 1825. It is said to have been first planted in Pauoa Valley on the island of Oahu. It is a medium-sized tree, well adapted to home grounds planting and grows quite rapidly in sunny locations in fertile, well-drained soils.

The fruit varies in size, shape, color, and flavor. Its leathery skin ranges from green to purplish black in color-depending on the state of maturity. The skin may be either smooth and thin or warty and hard, depending on the type. The flesh of the fruit is greenish-yellow to bright yellow when ripe and is oily and high in carbohydrates, vitamins and proteins. No other fruit, except perhaps the olive, contains as high a percentage of fat as the Avocado.

THREE TYPES AND THEIR HYBRIDS

Avocado in Hawaii belongs to three types: Guatemalan, West Indian, Mexican and their hybrids. The Guatemalan type is native to Ecuador, Nicaragua, Mexico and Central America and is more resistant to cold than the East Indian. Young leaves of this type are characteristically bronze or reddish in color. The skin of the fruit is usually thick, woody or rough. The fruit matures during the winter and spring months, is usually large and borne on long stems. The seed is small and fits tightly in its cavity.

Native to the lowlands of Central and South America, the West Indian type was introduced to the West Indies by the early Spaniards.

These trees are usually sensitive to cold. The skin of the fruit is characteristically smooth and green. The fruit matures in the summer and fall months and contains a large seed that fits loosely in its cavity.

The highlands of Mexico and the Andes Mountains are the home of the Mexican type of Avocado. The small leaves and young fruit have a characteristic anise odor. The smooth, thin-skinned fruit is small, rarely weighing a pound each.

The period during which any Avocado comes into fruit production varies according to variety and is also somewhat influenced by the elevation and temperature.

All varieties belong to one of two groups classified according to normal flowering time and sequence of opening and closing of blossoms. In one group, the flowers open in the forenoon when the pistil is receptive but pollen is not discharged. In the second group, the flowers open in the afternoon. There is a second flower opening period in both groups when pollen is shed but pistils are not receptive. Despite this phenomenon cross-pollination or fertilization can take place.

PROPAGATION

Plants should not be propagated from seed as some varieties do not reproduce true. Although plants can be propagated by cuttings or air-layering, these methods are not recommended. Budding and grafting are the common methods of propagating Avocado. However, grafting is the more popular method and may be executed in many ways. Whip or side wedge methods of grafting are among the most widely used. Whip grafting is the more exacting technique of the two.

Gardeners not wishing to be bothered with propagating plants can usually find a good selection at local nurseries. These plants, often grown in gallon tins or larger containers, are ready to plant. There is usually a good collection of varieties to choose from. Ask the nurseryman or your local agent for the variety best suited to your growing conditions. Choose the most vigorous plant, being sure that the graft union is completely healed over.

WHERE AND HOW TO PLANT

Variety is the main consideration in determining planting distances between trees. Soil considerations, elevation and precipitation are other aspects to consider. However, in any case, plants should be spaced at least 25 feet apart for best accommodation when trees are fully grown.

The hole should be at least four or five times larger than the container in which the plants were grown. Select a spot that receives maximum exposure to sunshine. If soil is poor, as is often times the case in new residential areas, replace it with an equal mixture of rich, loose top soil and compost. A couple of handfuls of fruit tree fertilizer should also be added.

The plant may be removed quite easily if first soaked in water and given a few taps to loosen it from its container. Do this rather carefully, as any disturbance to the root system can cause setback to the plant. When done correctly, the plant will separate from the container intact with its soil ball.

Position the plant at about the same level as it was in its container and fill the surrounding hole with good soil. Place a ring of fertilizer on the soil surface about six inches from the plant and follow with a good irrigation. The plant may need to be supported with a stake or protected with a section of paper or burlap bag for the first few days. These may be removed after the plant has begun to show signs of growth.

Cultivation for weed control should be as shallow as possible to avoid damaging the shallow root system. Mulching is recommended to control weeds.

FERTILIZING

For best results, the young plant should be fed often with a complete fertilizer at regular intervals. A fruit tree fertilizer can be used to good advantage. However, to eliminate guesswork, have the soil analyzed and use its analysis as a guide. The soil analysis will include information on amounts and kinds of fertilizers needed. Your local county agent can render valuable assistance.

A recommended schedule for the first year is to apply about a quarter pound of fertilizer four months after planting. This amount should be doubled eight months later. The fertilizer may be scratched into the surface inch of soil and followed with a good soaking of water. The second year schedule of fertilizer should total about two pounds applied in three doses at four month intervals. Increase the amounts of fertilizer gradually with each succeeding year.

Older trees should receive one or two pounds of fertilizer for each diameter inch of trunk applied at least twice annually. The first dose should be given just before blossoms form and the second after the last fruits have been harvested. For best results, apply the fertilizer in holes following the drip line of the tree. Water the fertilizer before covering the holes with soil.

After trees have grown to bearing size, most gardeners neglect to fertilize them. This is oftentimes reflected in the poor and unthrifty appearance of the trees. Remember that any tree will produce only as well as the care it receives.

INSECT PESTS

The most important insect pests of Avocado are beetles, mites, scales and thrips. Beetles like to feed on young plants, or the tender leaves of older trees.

Although their natural parasites usually keep them in check, scales can sometimes be a problem. Use a pesticide such as Malathion plus a sticking agent to control these pests. Spray may be applied to within 7 days of harvest, but not during blooming period.

Generally speaking, diseases are quite uncommon to Avocado. A resistant variety grown on good rootstocks is excellent insurance against disease. Avocado grown in good soil that drains well is also unlikely to suffer from diseases. Proper sanitation also helps ward off disease attacks. Fungus diseases that bother fruit may be checked with sprays containing 4 tablespoons of basic copper sulphate in a gallon of water.

BANANA

The Banana, of which there are some 300 edible forms, is native to the East Indies and the Tropics, where it is one of the most common fruits. Besides the fruit, popularly used as human food, the Banana plant has many different uses such as for house roofing, livestock feed, clothing, packing material, containers, cigarette paper, twine, medicine, dye and irrigation flumes. The fruit may be eaten fresh or cooked and is a source of alcohol, vinegar and wine.

The Banana is among the tallest of the herbs with stems or leaf sheaths rising as high as 20 feet and large foliage towering even higher. Each plant produces one inflorescence and reproduces by suckers around the base. There were some 70 varieties known to the old Hawaiians. Many of these have disappeared but many others have been introduced as replacements.

Among the most common varieties in Hawaii are the Cavendish or Chinese, the Bluefield or Gros Michel and the Brazilian Apple Banana. The Chinese variety is a low growing form, rising some six feet high and is well-suited to areas buffeted by strong winds. The Bluefield and Brazilian varieties are tall growing forms and, because of their height, are subject to wind damage. They may be successfully grown in protected pockets or in open areas with windbreaks. In the home grounds, they should be planted to the leeward side of the house.

PROPAGATION

Good eating Bananas do not produce seed but easily propagate from suckers originating from the base of old plants. New plants, best started

11

from selected large suckers, average about four to five feet in height. These may be removed from the established clump with a pick, spade or some sharp tool inserted between the parent plant and the young offshoot. Although the sucker may be planted immediately into its permanent location, it is customary to let it dry first, in order to minimize chances for rot. The older leaves of the new plant should be removed, leaving only those at the tip, to prevent excessive loss of moisture from transpiration. It is well to remember that the larger the sucker, the sooner the plant comes into fruit.

PLANTING

After the cut surface has dried or is sufficiently healed, the sucker may be planted in place. Bananas will do well in almost any location, provided they receive proper moisture. The soil need not be well-drained as the plant is somewhat tolerant to very wet conditions. The plant does best in the lowlands in open sun, although it also grows in partial shade. It thrives under warm conditions and will grow slowly in the cool of the uplands where ripening of the fruit may become a problem.

Holes to accommodate new plants should be at least two feet wide and two feet deep. If the soil is poor, improve it by mixing a large amount of compost and other decayed organic matter plus three or four handfuls of a complete fertilizer. The root end of the plant should be imbedded at least a foot in the hole. Fill the hole with soil, ring the plant with a thin band of fertilizer and water thoroughly. If the plant is top heavy, it may need to be staked to hold it upright until new roots develop. For the dwarf types, plants may be spaced about six feet apart, but for the tall varieties, the distance between plants should be doubled.

Given ample moisture, the new plant should make quite rapid growth. Since the Banana is shallow-rooted, the soil surface should be disturbed as little as possible. Weeds should be destroyed as soon as they appear and not allowed to mature.

FERTILIZING

One month after planting, apply a fertilizer such as 10-5-20 or 15-5-25 by scratching it into the soil surface some distance away from the plant. Follow with a good irrigation of water. Repeat the fertilization at the end of another four months and continue this schedule thereafter, gradually increasing the amount of fertilizer applied each time.

Bananas succeed best with regular applications of complete fertilizers coupled with generous amounts of water. Fortify the fertilizer applications with extra amounts of potash, as this practice has proven beneficial from experience. Analyzing the soil to get a true picture of its fertility level is recommended. Consult your local county agent who will furnish information on proper soil sampling procedures and recommendations.

The size, quantity and quality of the fruit is dependent on the fertility of the soil and the number of plants in each clump. No more than three plants should be allowed to grow in each clump--all others should be removed. A good practice to follow is to allow one sucker to grow every four months and to prune off all others. The removed plants may be used to start other clumps. Limiting the number assures all plants in the clump their full share of moisture and plant nutrients. They are then able to make full growth resulting in maximum production of fruit.

In about a year's time, the plant should be of bearing size. The fruit bunch has set when blossoms begin to fall. At this stage, the large bud at the tip of the fruiting stalk may be removed. In some locations, such as wet areas, the bunch is usually covered with a large paper or perforated plastic sack to protect it from insect pests and bruising.

When individual fruit is nice and round or shows tinges of yellow, the bunch is ready to be harvested. In tall varieties, carefully hack the middle of the plant to lower the fruit bunch for more convenient handling. Cut off the bunch with a long stem to facilitate handling. After the fruit has been removed, the old plant should be chopped close to the ground and cut into convenient sections for final disposal. The fruit may be allowed to ripen as a bunch or divided into hands, whichever is most convenient. Keep the fruit in a dark, warm, humid corner where it will ripen quickly. Fruit left on the tree to ripen can suffer damage by the Oriental fruit fly. It is best to harvest when the fruit is in the mature green stage, before the fruit fly deposits its eggs.

DISEASES AND INSECTS

One of the most serious diseases of Banana is the so-called Panama wilt disease. The symptoms may be mistaken for those of other Banana diseases. The lower leaves are usually yellow and wilted. The mature tissues within the stem of older plants are usually discolored. A cross-section of the stem will show a ring of discoloration in young plants and complete discoloration in fruit-bearing plants. Fruits of diseased plants show no discoloration whatsoever. (Moko and heart-rot diseases have somewhat similar symptoms to Panama wilt.)

Another symptom of clumps affected by Panama disease is the abundance of new suckers that never reach maturity. Because the fungus that causes Panama disease lives in the soil for many years, any form of cultivation that might cause root damage should be avoided. Planting material from diseased clumps should never be used to plant new areas. Any equipment used on diseased plants should be thoroughly cleaned before being used in other areas. The equipment may be washed and disinfected with 10 percent formaldehyde.

Disease resistant varieties such as the Lacatan and Williams Hybrid were introduced to replace the highly susceptible Bluefield. The Williams Hybrid Banana, introduced to Hawaii from Australia in 1954, originated as a sport in a commercial planting of the Chinese variety in New South Wales. Resistant to Panama disease, it is a vigorous grower and produces good quality fruit even under unfavorable conditions. Its fruit is somewhat superior to the Chinese variety both in flavor and appearance. Mature plants range from 7 to 12 feet in height and fruit bunches are comparatively larger than those of its parent.

A disease common to Chinese banana is finger tip rot, which starts with the flowers and advances to the skin of the fruit and eventually

13

into the pulp. Spray fruits and foliage bi-weekly with a fungicide such as Maneb. Include a sticking agent for best results.

Common to Chinese banana growing in wet areas is the Freckle disease. The damage occurs as freckles on the leaves and fruit. It may be controlled by wrapping the fruit bunch with a paper or perforated plastic sack or spraying with a Bordeaux mixture formulated by mixing one pound of copper sulphate and one pound of lime with 12 gallons of water or spraying with a fungicide such as Maneb.

Plant suckers affected by nematodes, a tiny, worm-like animal, will cause roots to form small knots and thus interfere with their normal function. Areas suspected to have nematode infestation should be avoided. Another effective control method is to fumigate the soil with a commercial nematocide. This is a rather involved operation requiring the use of poisonous gas and fumigation equipment. Consult your local county agent for assistance.

Plant clean rhizomes by trimming roots or suckers and immersing in hot water at 122°F for 10 to 15 minutes. A solution made up of one part chlorine bleach and five parts water may also be beneficial as a dip.

Black Leaf Streak attacks the leaves, yellowing them and producing lesions. An oil-fungicide combination spray will help control the disease and clean cultural practices will prevent its spread.

Bunchy Top Virus is one of the most serious diseases of bananas. Darker green streaks appear on the lower portion of the midrib. When fruit is produced some fruits may be twisted. Suckers developing after infection are stunted, with leaves bunched at the top of the stem. These plants will not produce fruit. The virus is spread by the banana aphid. Use a systemic insecticide for aphid control, which is essential in controlling the disease. Infected plants must be destroyed, but homeowners should not attempt to dispose of suspect plants. Contact your local county extension agent with questions. Your help in reporting this disease is vital to efforts to protect Hawaii's banana industry.

The Banana, both dwarf and tall varieties, is a good addition to the home grounds and with proper placement enhances the landscaping. The fruit is an economical and nutritious food. Varieties that produce colored or variegated fruit are a novelty and, therefore, can become a focal point in the home grounds planting. Dwarf forms may be planted to complement a low house and are quite handsome when in fruit. The tall varieties may be planted to best advantage at the corners of the home, lot or next to a high house where they will receive protection from high winds.

BIRD-OF-PARADISE

One of the most remarkable of exotic flowering plants is the Bird-of-Paradise *(Strelitzia reginae)*, a native of South Africa. It belongs to a genus that includes four other species and is named after the wife of King George III, Charlotte Sophia, of the Mecklinburgh-Strelitz family.

An aristocrat of the garden, the Bird-of-Paradise is slow-growing and trunkless with compact cluster of large stiff, leathery, bluish-gray foliage. The highly attractive flowers of orange, yellow, and blue are distinctive and dramatic and may rise five feet or as high as the leaves. Once established, it has few peers as a year-round source of beautiful blossoms. The flowers are not only long-lasting, but excellent for indoor display in silhouette arrangement. Used by themselves as cut flowers and complemented by their own leaves, Bird-of-Paradise makes a complete picture. They can be combined with figurines, driftwood, fruits, foliage and other flowers to enhance special arrangements. Flowers will stay alive for nearly two weeks when water is changed regularly.

PROPAGATION
The plant can be propagated from seed, from clump divisions or from started seedlings in containers of various sizes available from garden supply houses. Since seeds have a tough outer covering, they should first be scarified before planting to hasten germination. Plant seeds in a propagation of flat loose, fertile soil and keep moist in a corner of the garden. In about a month, young seedlings should be emerging from the soil.

Irrigate seedlings with water containing a small amount of fertilizer to hasten growth. When plants have about four or five leaves, they are ready for transplanting into individual containers. These may be quart or gallon size cans. Use media containing equal parts fertile top soil and compost to which a small amount of fertilizer has been added. If small containers are used in the beginning, plants may be transplanted into succeedingly larger pots. As the plants become root-bound, they are ready for transfer to their permanent location. Plants propagated from seed require at least three years before they will begin to flower.

If plants are to be propagated from sections of old established clumps, use a sharp tool to make clean cuts. The divisions should have some attached roots otherwise they will not grow. Also, secure divisions preferably from protruding sections of the clump. The cut sections should be treated with sulphur to hasten healing. The preferred time for taking clump divisions is during the cool months of the year. Clump divisions usually flower faster than plants grown from seed.

Probably the most convenient method for propagating Bird-of-Paradise is through purchase of potted seedlings from garden supply stores. These are priced according to the size of plants and are comparatively cheap.

Bird-of-Paradise prefer sunshine for best growth. They will thrive in loose, fertile soil with good drainage. They also demand ample moisture but plants will suffer in water-logged media.

For specimen plants in the garden, dig holes at least 18 inches deep and 18 inches wide. If soil is poor, replace with a mixture of equal parts black sand and fertile top soil. Place plant in the middle of the hole, cover to ground level, and then ring it with a small band of general garden fertilizer. Follow this operation with a generous amount of water. For planting as a hedge by itself, or next to a wall or fence, Bird-of-Paradise is usually handsome. Since clumps grow to great size when left undisturbed, plants should be spaced no less than four feet apart in rows.

If specimens are to be grown in containers, use cans, tubs, or pots no smaller than 12 inches across the top. Large containers eliminate the necessity for frequent repotting. Fill pots with specially prepared media containing equal parts rich top soil, compost and black sand. For good drainage, place a two-inch layer of coarse gravel in the bottom of the container.

Plants should receive general garden fertilizer at least twice a year to keep them growing in tip-top condition. The amount should be gradually increased with each succeeding year. For quick results, use a soluble fertilizer. Once the plants have become established they should not be disturbed as any interference tends to set back growth with resulting decrease in flower production. Old leaves may be removed as they dry up to enhance the general good appearance of the plant.

One of the nicest things about growing Bird-of-Paradise is that they are seldom attacked by insect or disease pests. However, an occasional spray with a combination insecticide will help to ward off any prospective pest build-up.

16

Soil should be sterilized or fumigated where there is incidence of root rot. There are any number of chemicals available from garden houses suitable for fumigating soil. Since diseases may also be carried by plants, use only clean and disease-free stock.

CUT FLOWERS

The older the plants become, the more flowers they produce. Harvesting of blossoms may begin as soon as the first florets appear. Flowers should preferably be cut in the late afternoon when they have the greatest accumulation of food and water. This extra food supply will help them last longer as cut flowers. Flowers may also be cut in the early morning. Use a sharp cutting instrument and sever off flower stalks at an angle. The angular cut exposes a greater surface through which water may be absorbed. A dull instrument could plug up the tubes and flatten the vessels through which water is taken up the flower stalk. For best results, always have cut ends immersed in water after separation from the mother plant. To prolong life of cut flowers, snip off 1/4 inch from the end every other day with a razor blade or sharp instrument.

Dipping stem ends in hot water or singeing them over a flame causes water in stems to expand. This serves to force air out and facilitates water intake. Splitting the cut end to increase the water-absorbing surface is also helpful. Flowers that are handled gently and as little as possible last longer than those treated carelessly.

Since Bird-of-Paradise is quite easily hybridized, there are now any number of varieties superior to the normal form. A fancier in Wahiawa has developed a variety that produces larger flowers with a greater number of florets. He claims that his variety also lasts longer as cut flowers.

BONSAI

Bonsai may be defined as the creation of plants into certain forms to describe nature in miniature according to Japanese standards. It also may be described as a miniature potted tree trained in a certain manner. Bonsai culture has been practiced in Japan for some 900 years, but it was not until after World War II that it became popular in the U.S.

Generally speaking, Bonsai are quite hardy and can withstand some neglect. However, to be at their best, they need close attention and care. They thrive best under natural conditions in limited shade out in the open. The plants are excellent for indoor display but can take only a limited amount of this type of treatment. If Bonsai are taken inside the home, they should not be left indoors longer than 48 hours, otherwise the plants will begin to suffer. A preferred method would be to rotate and change specimens every other day.

BONSAI NEED WATER

Bonsai need more water than they usually receive. The plants should be thoroughly soaked each time, but making sure that the excess water is removed through the drainage holes in the bottom of the pot. However, roots should never be water-logged; otherwise, they will drown. A soil that retains moisture but drains easily is best. A loose soil permits the entry of air so essential to the life and proper functioning of roots.

A good method of watering Bonsai is to soak plants and containers in a tub or pan a couple of inches above the soil line for about 10 or 15 minutes. This practice lessens the chances of loss of soil that so often occurs when Bonsai are watered by means of a hose with a sprinkle head.

Apply fertilizer at least four times a year, starting when new growth begins to appear and repeating every couple or three months thereafter.

PRUNING AND REPOTTING

All growth that does not compliment the appearance of the Bonsai should be removed. Side shoots that appear on the main trunk may be pulled off if they interfere with the lines of the plant.

Because Bonsai are grown in small containers that confine or restrict natural root development, they need to be repotted periodically. The plants should be repotted when they become root-bound. This condition exists when the plant roots have extended themselves to a point where they are no longer able to get any nourishment from the soil. Repotting plants also helps improve root aeration and drainage and also supplies new soil into which the new roots can grow. Pruning old roots helps development of new roots, thus helping to keep the plant root system always young.

The ideal time to prune old roots and repot is early in the year when new growth is just beginning. However, if repotting involves only transplanting to a new or larger container, this can be done any time it is convenient to do so. This operation is best carried out in the shade on a cloudy day.

After taking the plant or tree out of the container, clean it out thoroughly. Use a chopstick or brush to remove the soil from the plant and its container. In trimming the roots, use large, sharp scissors. Cut away one third of the side roots and about one half of the bottom.

If the container top is round or square, place the tree or plant in the middle. However, if it is oval or rectangular, place it one third from the far side. Whether the container is deep or shallow, the tree will need to be supported in place. Strong cord or plastic strips may be used to brace the plant in the position it is to occupy. After the plant has developed a sufficiently strong root system, the supports may be cut off or removed in such a fashion that does not interfere with root growth.

After the plant has been secured in place, soil should be added to fill the container and the crevices between and under the roots of the tree. The new soil should be a dry, sifted mixture of equal parts top soil, compost, peat moss and black sand. A chopstick may be used to fill the spaces with the soil. When sufficient soil has been added so that the container can no longer hold any more, brush away the excess from the top. A container that is filled with soil to the very top will be difficult to water, so keep the soil line about 1/4 inch below the rim. A generous application of water should follow.

Place the newly repotted plant in partial shade until it begins to show signs of new growth. It can then be exposed to full sun for a few hours each day until it has become accustomed to the natural conditions. While this is being done, never let the plant go dry; otherwise, it may suffer setback.

CONTAINERS

One of the main objectives of Bonsai is to suggest nature in its various moods. Therefore, the selection of the proper containers to harmonize with this purpose is very important. The containers should supplement rather than detract from the beauty of the Bonsai. Subdued colors and simple forms are the most appropriate. The containers should never dwarf the tree and should be of a shape that is not distracting.

Pottery containers with drainage holes are the most popular. They should never be glazed inside but may be glazed or unglazed on the outside. A container that is carefully selected can mean the difference between success and failure in the creation of prize-winning Bonsai. Local nurseries and garden shops carry a good selection to choose from.

The choice of plants that may be fashioned into Bonsai is almost limitless. Among the most popular are flowering trees and shrubs, conifers, pines and many tropical plants.

TRAINING BONSAI

The artistic shape of Bonsai is achieved only through continuous training and pruning of the stems and branches. The ideal or artistic proportion for large tall-growing specimens is 80 percent tree and 20 percent container. For low spreading trees or dwarf shrubs, the proportion should be 60 percent for the plant and 40 percent for the container.

Branches may be trained into desired shape with the aid of rubber-insulated copper wire and lead weights. The wire is wound around the trunk or branch to hold them in the desired position. They are only removed after the plant has begun to grow in the desired shape.

Bonsai are best displayed outdoors on an elevated stand that receives partial shade during the day. Specimens may be grouped according to size and type of plant. Bonsai displayed on stands are not only attractive but it makes it easier to care for them. They can be inspected more readily for signs of pests.

During hot weather, Bonsai can be cooled and benefit from an extra fine mist spray left on for two or three hours. The special nozzles emit a fine mist that consumes very little water. This cools and helps humidify the surrounding atmosphere.

Some practitioners grow a very fine moss as a ground cover for their Bonsai. With this type of ground cover, the Bonsai may be hilled up to a slope without any danger of loss of soil. The ground cover enhances the appearance of the Bonsai.

BOUGAINVILLEA

The Bougainvillea is a hardy, climbing, shrubby plant from Brazil that belongs to the *Nyctaginaceae* family. It is named after Louis A. de Bougainville, a French navigator who found it in Rio de Janeiro. It is an aggressive, large woody vine with thorny, strong, rapid-growing stems. Leaves are ovate, alternate and hairy, and the tiny flowers are grouped in large, massed clusters. The small inconspicuous tubular blossoms are surrounded by three large colored bracts that form the decorative feature of the plant.

For large expanses of difficult-to-maintain areas, Bougainvillea is nigh unbeatable as a ground cover. It can cover a whole hillside and will choke out weed growth very well. It needs no pruning except in spots where it might interfere with a cultivated area. It becomes a mass of color with much eye appeal during the flowering season.

As a specimen plant pruned to tree-like form, it is a focal point of beauty when grown either in the garden or in containers. Pruned to a single stem, Bougainvillea can be converted into many forms, including one resembling a tree. It can be trained as an espalier or sheared into other formal forms, depending on the gardener's imagination and ingenuity.

A most remarkably adaptable plant, Bougainvillea can be grown under dry, arid conditions or in areas of abundant moisture. Once started, it will survive in poor tight soils or thrive in an ideal mixture of loose rich top soil with generous amounts of organic matter. It prefers full sun where it will be most floriferous but also grows in varying degrees of shade.

PROPAGATION

Although a rank grower, the plant poses some problems in propagation. The most popular method is by selected cuttings. Young, fast growing shoots seldom take root as cuttings and should be avoided. Instead, choose slow-growing, thin-stemmed, semi-woody branches from 6 to 8 inches long. In observation tests, these have proven to be most successful for propagation purposes. Although it is also possible to use thick, woody cuttings, success with them is limited.

The home gardener with limited equipment can use a propagation flat or gallon can to good advantage. Use sterile media such as vermiculite or clean sand. Dust lower ends of the cuttings with a commercial rooting compound before inserting them to about half their length in the moist propagating media. Remove lower leaves and cover the container with a plastic film to reduce evaporation, produce humidity and heat. Under such conditions, the media will not need to be watered as often as when left uncovered. In a few weeks, the cuttings will produce new shoots. The plastic covering may then be left off and the cuttings allowed to grow to good size before transplanting.

Soak the growing plants before beginning the transplanting operation. Young Bougainvillea plants are very sensitive and should be handled with extreme care when being transferred. Transplanting is best done in the shade. Remove plants very carefully from the growing media, making sure that the young plant's fine roots are disturbed as little as possible. Transfer preferably to a paper or peat pot to avoid any further disturbance of the root system in the future. Use a fertilized mixture of top soil and compost. Soak transplants and leave in the shade for a few days until they recover from the shock. They may then be gradually exposed to more sunshine until they are hardened to their new environment.

A very convenient method for propagating a limited number of plants is by ground layering. Select a woody branch, one preferably growing close to the ground, and secure it in place by tying it with a piece of twine. Remove a small ring of bark from the branch and cover this area with a mount of moistened soil. In a few weeks, roots will form near the girdled area. Allow branch to develop strong roots after which it may be separated from the mother plant. Nurse the plant along for a time until it is able to grow by itself. It may then be uprooted carefully for transplanting. Remove most of the older leaves and give the plant a good irrigation.

Roots of established specimens may be used to propagate new plants. Sever a few strong roots with a pick and, in time, they will spring new plant shoots. Allow these to grow to good size before uprooting for transplanting in the approved manner.

Individual plants need much room in which to spread when grown out in the open. Planting holes a foot across should be dug at least 12 inches deep. Place plants in the middle of the hole and cover to ground level with loose, fertile soil. Irrigate and keep plants moist until they show signs of growth.

Although Bougainvillea can stand neglect after becoming established, it will benefit from applications of general garden fertilizer at least twice a year. Always cultivate fertilizer into soil surface and follow with irrigation for best effect. The plant is remarkably free from pests but, for insurance, a general purpose insecticide spray may be applied occasionally.

VARIETIES

Among the most popular of the named varieties of Bougainvillea are *glabra* with carmine-rose bracts, *variegate* with leaves of creamy-white markings, *spectabilis* with rose-colored bracts, *sanderiana* with rich rose-red bracts, *Crimson Lake* with bright crimson bracts, *Mrs. Butt* with deep rose-red bracts, *lateritia* with brick-red bracts, *Harrisii* with dark green foliage variegated with creamy-white bracts, *parviflora* with purple bracts, and an all-white form.

Foster Garden in Honolulu since 1959 has imported, received as gifts, or in exchange, more then 80 different named varieties of Bougainvillea. Most of these introductions have come from Nairobi, Africa, and a very few from Thailand, Philippines, India, and the Monrovia Nursery in California. Most of these arrived as cuttings, some rooted, other as plants, and a few as seeds.

Among the most spectacular is *B. Carmencita*, a recently patented plant discovered by Ted Green, who claims it as a new and distinct variety characterized by a novel tripling of the bracts. It originated as a sport discovered in the Philippines. The original sport was a mutant branch on *B. spectabilis v. Crimson Lake* and differed from the parent by having multiple bracts. The sport produces rose-colored bracts in multiples of three that arise where a flower is normally borne. No flowers are produced, and the size of the bracts decreases through each tripling.

CITRUS

Handsome plants, excellent for landscaping and that produce highly fragrant flowers and deliciously nutritious fruit, are among some of the many benefits you derive from growing Citrus. The Citrus is native to Asia and has been in cultivation for several centuries. The fruit is attractive and, depending on variety, ranges in size from peewees of less than an ounce apiece to jumbos of several pounds each. It is widely used fresh or processed. Oils, pectins, flavorings, perfumes and other by-products are derived from the blossoms and fruit.

The first Citrus fruit was introduced to Kona, Hawaii, in 1792. Later introductions to Niihau, in all probability, came from Tahiti.

GROWN IN THE OPEN OR IN CONTAINERS

Citrus may be grown out in the open or in containers. In recent years, dwarf Citrus have become popular for growing in limited space out in the open, or as tubbed specimens in patios. Dwarf Citrus occupy only about a quarter of the space needed to grow commercial orchard varieties that usually have to be spaced from 25 to 30 feet apart. A full-grown dwarf variety will grow to a maximum height of only eight feet in the open and less in tubs or containers.

Because of their compact size, dwarf Citrus are quite decorative and lend themselves admirably to container culture. However, they may be grown out in the open as specimen or hedge plants to beautify the home grounds. For a unique and ornamental effect, they can be trained into espaliers against a blank wall or fence. They are also grown on trellises or in other more formal designs.

There are many types of Citrus suitable for outdoors or container culture. Among these are grapefruit, lemon, sour orange, lime, tangerine or Mandarin orange, shaddock, sweet orange and hybrids such as tangelo, citrange and limequats, to name the most important.

PROPAGATION

No matter where grown, Citrus requires plenty of sunshine for best growth. Citrus can be propagated from seed, but since seedling plants do not always produce true, this method is not commonly used. Seedling plants are often used as stock on which to graft scions of outstanding plants. The seedling plants are usually from varieties with vigorous root systems tolerant to soil pests. The most popular methods of propagating citrus are budding, grafting or air-layering.

For the home gardener, it would be more convenient to purchase recommended varieties from nurserymen. The cost of plants is usually nominal. For more detailed information on varieties for specific uses, consult your local Extension County Agent or nurseryman.

PLANTING

Large commercial varieties for outdoor planting should be spaced at least 25 feet apart. Dwarf varieties may be planted closer to each other.

For outdoor planting, dig a hole thrice as wide and twice as deep as the container in which the plant is growing. Fill the hole with a mixture of fertile top soil and compost fortified with a small amount of fruit tree fertilizer.

To remove the plant from its container faster, soak in water and tap the sides until it slips off easily. The plant, with its soil ball intact, should then be transferred to the hole and planted at the same level as it was in the container. Follow with a good irrigation and keep the plant protected for the first few days until it has become adjusted to its new location.

Citrus require large amounts of water, but will do poorly under waterlogged conditions. Irrigate regularly so that the soil never dries out completely. Use mulch to conserve moisture, reduce frequency of irrigation, and lessen weed growth.

FERTILIZING

Fertilizers recommended for fruit trees should be applied at least twice a year. Start with about a quarter pound for the first year after transplanting and increase this amount gradually as the tree increases in size. Since fruit production is dependent on the condition of the foliage, the fertilizer applications should be supplemented with some nitrogen fertilizer. Nitrogen promotes greenness and vegetative growth.

For the first few years, the fertilizer may be cultivated into the soil surface and followed with a good soaking of water. Older or larger trees need to be fed at least a pound of fruit tree fertilizer for each diameter inch of tree trunk. This should be applied in holes spaced about 18 inches apart following the dripline of the tree. The holes should be about an inch wide and at least six inches deep. A soil augur, or pointed end of a pickax may be used for digging the holes. Water the fertilizer before covering the holes with soil.

Citrus seldom require pruning because they shape up naturally. However, excess branches should be removed to promote air circulation. This reduces the chances for a buildup of pests.

DISEASES AND INSECTS

Insects which attack citrus include scales, Chinese rose beetles, citrus swallowtail, thrips, aphids and whiteflies. Pesticide sprays in combination with a petroleum type spray oil are effective in controlling these pests and may be sprayed to within 7 days of harvest. Do not spray during blooming season. Be sure to follow instructions on the container.

Although viruses are often found in citrus there is presently no effective control of these diseases. Other diseases affecting citrus are scab, melanose, algal spot and sooty mold, which can be controlled with fungicide sprays such as copper compunds. Controlling insects such as scales, whiteflies and aphids can eliminate problems with sooty mold.

Chlorosis, a yellowing of the leaves, indicating minor elemental deficiency, can be corrected with soil or foliar spray applications of chelated iron, manganese and zinc.

CONTAINER CULTURE

For container culture use pots, boxes or tubs from 14 to 18 inches across and about 20 inches deep. These are large enough to accommodate plants for several years. Use a half and half mixture of good top soil and humus plus a small amount of fruit tree fertilizer. Fill the container with this mixture to about three inches from the top. Transplant the citrus, and to insure good drainage, plant it high.

Correct watering is an acquired skill. Watch for wilting new growth or cupping of leaves, which are all indicators of the need for water. Lack of water occurs when applied in insufficient amounts or not often enough. Be consistent, and water on a regular schedule. Be sure to apply enough water to soak the root zone. To lessen frequency of watering and discourage weed growth, mulch with gravel, pebbles or other convenient material.

Container-grown plants thrive on regular fertilization. For the first year, sprinkle a heaping tablespoonful of fruit tree fertilizer on the surface and follow with a good watering. Do this about once each month, adding a small amount of nitrogen fertilizer each time. Increase the amount gradually as the tree gets larger.

Younger trees may develop erratic branches and these should be cut back immediately. In time the tree will round out and shape up naturally without too much pruning. This can be hastened by pinching out the tips of new growth. Sucker growth produced below the graft should be removed as soon as they are noticed. These suckers are not only worthless but will sap vitality from the tree.

Trained as espaliers into formal or informal patterns, Citrus are dramatic, particularly when in fruit. They may be trained on a trellis, wall or fence, and can be held to any desired size by pruning. First decide the final size and form of the espalier, and build the wire framework or trellis to take care of it at maturity. An informal pattern is far easier to manage and can be trained on any type of support.

Depending on the size of the espalier, grow as many plants as will fill out the desired size. Tie the branches in the direction they are to grow and pinch or prune out all growth that doesn't conform to the design. Use raffia or some soft material to prevent injury to tied branches.

CROTON

The Croton *(Codiaeum variegatum)* belongs to the Spurge family *(Euphorbiaceae)*, which includes some 280 genera and about 7,000 species. There are some 125 varieties listed with pictures in the third edition of Exotica. It is a dwarf, woody shrub with foliage of many colors and shapes, commonly found in Malaya and the Pacific Islands. The wild, green-leaved form is native to Fiji and Australia. The attractive, bright-colored foliage of cultivated forms was developed mostly by mainland hybridists. The many varieties are probably from one botanical species greatly improved by selection and crossing.

The leaves are alternate, simple, and rather thick and leathery and the juice somewhat milky. They are of many forms and color patterns including, green, yellow, purple, orange, red and shades in between and may be plain, mottled or spotted. The thick, smooth, short-stemmed leaves are long or short and sometimes narrow, wrinkled, lobed, oblong, wavy or twisted.

The flowers are small and inconspicuous when compared to the foliage and are produced as long spikes in the axils of the upper leaves. Roots and leaves of the croton have been used as medicine. The foliage of some forms is cooked for greens and the young growth is used as livestock feed.

VALUED FOR FOLIAGE

Crotons are valued for the varied and brilliant markings of their foliage. The young leaves are usually green and yellow, but as they mature change to other shades and color combinations ranging from almost pure white to light and deep yellow, orange, pink, and red crimson. They may be grown as specimen, hedge, group or pot plants.

PROPAGATION

Crotons may be propagated from seed, cuttings, budding or air-layering. Ripe seeds, which look like tiny berries, may be planted in germination flats with special media. The media may be clean top soil mixed with compost, screened fern fiber or a commercial product, such as vermiculite or sponge rock.

Cover the seeds about 1/4 inch deep, water and keep in moderate shade. The seeds will germinate after seven days. The seedlings should receive a small amount of fertilizer with the irrigation water to promote rapid growth. After they have developed three or four pairs of true leaves, the seedlings should be moved out in full sun.

When the young plants have grown to fairly good size, they may be transplanted to individual paper or peat pots. Soak the flat with water to ease the removal of seedlings. The young plants may then be easily removed with a trowel and transferred to containers. If the roots are not severely disturbed, the plants will make rapid recovery. Otherwise, remove a few of the lower leaves to minimize setback.

When the plants are about a foot high, they may be transplanted to their permanent location. If they are to be grown for display, they may be transferred to larger size containers.

Crotons also may be quite readily propagated from cuttings. Best material are branches of about pencil thickness, although larger, older cuttings are also useable. Short branches about nine inches long are ideal but longer ones may be used. Remove leaves, dip the butt ends in a hormone rooting powder before imbedding the cuttings in the propagating media. Water thoroughly and keep in a semi-shady spot. Never allow cuttings to dry out, otherwise mortality will be high. Young growth will form after several weeks. When roots are quite strong, cuttings are ready for transplanting.

Branches to be air-layered may be of any size but ideally should be woody, 15-inch sections with a crown or growing point. With a sharp knife, scrape off about a 3/4-inch ring of bark. Moisten with a wad of sphagnum moss and wrap it around the scraped area. Cover the sphagnum moss with a sturdy pliable sheet of plastic material and tie both ends securely with twine. When a strong root system has formed, the branch may be severed from the mother plant. Carefully remove the plastic covering and transplant to a pot. The new plant should remain in the container until it is strong enough to be transplanted elsewhere.

When propagating material is scarce, budding may be employed to propagate plants of the desired variety. The budding should be done when plants are in active growth. The stock plant should be about 1/4 inch thick. With a sharp knife, make an inverted T-cut on the stock plant to accommodate the bud. Insert the bud into the cut by gently lifting the bark. When the bud is in place, seal with wax and wrap securely with raffia or masking tape. Do not cover the bud. Remove the tip of the growing point of the stock plant to force rapid growth in the bud. If the operation is successful, the bud will show signs of growth in a few weeks. The wrapping may be removed after the bud has begun to grow.

WHERE TO PLANT

Crotons will do well in almost any type of soil as long as it drains well. For hedges or group planting, dig and cultivate the soil to a depth of at least 15 inches. If soil is tight and sticky, mix with sufficient black sand or other coarse material plus some general garden fertilizer to correct the condition.

A sunny location is best, as some varieties will only produce their best color under full light. However, there are others with sensitive foliage that prefer partial shade or filtered light.

Crotons thrive in moist soil and should never be allowed to go for very long without moisture, otherwise growth will be stunted with resulting poor coloring and loss of foliage. Large plants naturally require more attention then small specimens.

When plants become leggy or too tall to be at their best, they may be pruned back to force new growth.

Plants grown in containers need to be repotted when they become root-bound. They should be transferred to larger containers with fresh media. If they are over-grown, excess branches and roots may be pruned before transplanting into new soil. Keep them moist and let stand in partial shade until new growth begins.

A constant supply of plant food is essential to the production of top grade plants. Fertilize garden grown specimens with a complete fertilizer every three months. The fertilizer may be scratched into the soil surface and watered in or applied with irrigation.

Pests should never be allowed to build up, otherwise control will be more difficult. A regular spraying program with a general purpose pesticide will help check insects. Do this at least once a month.

CROWN FLOWER

A great favorite of Queen Liliuokalani, the Crown Flower *(Calotropis gigantea)*, also known as the giant milkweed, or Pua Kalaunu in Hawaiian, is native to India, Iran, China and Tibet. It is a member of the Milkweed family *(Asclepiadaceae)* that includes some 220 genera with characteristic milky juice that is poisonous in some species.

It is a large shrub with white glaucous stems and distinctive star-like flowers that are said to be sacred to the Hindus. The flowers consist of a base of five thick, star-like, twisted petals from which arise a symmetrical crown-like structure at whose apex are stamens and a five-pointed style. The blossoms are carried in clusters at branch tips and have a pleasant, sweetish odor.

The lavender-flowered form was first introduced to Hawaii and was later followed by the white-flowered form in 1920. Leaves are pale-green, oval, thick, and almost stemless. The leaves, covered with white down, have some medicinal value as do the bark and roots. It blooms the year-round and is especially useful during periods when most flowers are in short supply. The blossoms are strung into leis.

The plant is quite hardy and does well under normal cultivation or under conditions of neglect. It is tolerant to various growing conditions ranging from poor soil in arid locations to fertile, well-drained loams in moist areas. It succeeds best in sunny spots but may be grown in some shade.

PROPAGATION

To propagate Crown Flower, cut wood branches, after removing leaves, into 12-inch sections. Allow cuttings to stop bleeding or heal, dust bottom tips with rooting hormone, and insert in a propagation flat containing black sand or an equal mixture of vermiculite and black sand. Cuttings may be spaced an inch apart and imbedded to about half their length. Give cuttings a thorough irrigation with water, after which the flat may be covered with a thin sheet of plastic. The covering will retard moisture evaporation, and also produce a humid condition ideal for plant growth. Apply water if growing media shows signs of drying. When cuttings have developed some foliage, the covering may be removed from the propagation flat. The cuttings may be transplanted after they have grown strong roots.

An excellent way to grow Crown Flower is as a hedge and as a source of blossoms. Planted in this manner, the plants serve as a barrier and also provide a supply of flowers. Since plants grow in a spreading fashion, they need to be spaced quite close to achieve the effect of a hedge.

For hedge planting, dig a 12-inch strip of soil at least 15 inches deep. Rooted foot-long cuttings may be planted a foot apart about four inches deep in this area. Spread two thin layers of general garden fertilizer about three inches away from the cuttings. Cover the fertilizer with some soil and follow with a good irrigation.

Keep plants moist but not waterlogged until they pick up, after which they can receive less frequent watering. Two months after planting, spread a thin ring of fertilizer around the plants just before an irrigation; this will help stimulate plant growth. This schedule of fertilization should be followed regularly every other month thereafter until plants are about five feet high.

PRUNING

When plants are about three feet high, they should be given a light pruning. Removing the growing tips will encourage branching, which is essential to thick plant growth.

When plants have grown to about five feet high, they may be given another pruning. At six feet high, only straggly side branches should be removed. Depending on the available space, the hedge may be trimmed vertically to about two feet in width. This is about the ideal width for a hedge, but if the gardener so desires, he can trim it closer or allow it to grow wider.

The top growth should not be pruned, but allowed to produce flowers. However, if plants grow too tall, making harvesting of blossoms difficult, they may be cut back gradually. This is best done by pruning back half of the tall growing branches. When these have produced side branches and are well on their way to producing another crop of flower buds, the remaining branches may be cut back. If this practice is followed, there will never be a period when the hedge will not have some flowers.

After the hedge has become established, it may receive less fertilizer. Over-fertilization, especially with formulae containing high amounts of nitrogen, will stimulate foliage growth at the expense of flower formation.

To achieve a rather novel effect, scions of the lavender form may be grafted onto stock of the white form or vice versa. This is best accomplished on bushes about five feet high. The operation can be easily carried out because of the convenient height. Branches about the thickness of a large pencil are best. With a sharp knife, make a V-cut after removing the top of the branch. Into this cut, insert the scion, the bottom of which has been fashioned into a wedge to fit snugly into it. The union should be secured firmly with masking tape. A good scheme is to graft about one half of the bush. At blossoming time, one half of the plant will sport white flowers while the remainder will have lavender blossoms. However, care must be exercised at pruning time to be sure that the grafted branches are not removed below the union. The masking tape should remain, or be replaced with something more durable, to serve as a reminder at pruning time.

PESTS OF THE CROWN FLOWER

Insect pests potentially harmful to Crown Flower include mites, aphids, mealy bugs, and scales. Diseases are few and seldom troublesome. Mites are very minute and have sucking organs with which they suck juices from plant tissue, causing the affected parts to become grayish in color. The insects usually assume the color of their food supply, and are often identified by the webbing they produce. Malathion applied according to directions on the label is an effective control.

Aphids, sometimes called plant lice, are visible to the naked eye. The insects possess sucking mouth parts, and are most active on the young growing parts of the plant. The injured parts fail to develop, and the growing leaf or bud becomes wrinkled or distorted.

Mealy bugs appear as white cottony masses on the plant. The eggs are laid in the cottony mass and, upon hatching, the young move about the plants. The young mealy bugs, in turn, are transported by ants from plant to plant.

Scale insects differ greatly in size and shape, and are either hard-shelled or soft-shelled types. The adults are usually covered by a brownish, shiny, or white cottony covering. In the early stages, the young move about but later become stationary when they develop the scale coating.

GARDENIA

There are two types of Gardenias commonly grown as ornamental shrubs in Hawaii. The more popular of the two is *Gardenia jasminoides*, which produces either single or double waxy flowers that are highly fragrant. The other is *Gardenia taitensis* that bears scented but single flowers. The Gardenia belongs to the Coffee family *(Rubiaceae)*, and is named after Dr. Alexander Garden.

G. jasminoides, sometimes known as Cape Jasmine, is native to China and is a short shrub with shiny evergreen leaves that are pointed at both ends. The flowers are white upon opening but turn yellowish afterwards. Blossoms are used for cut flowers, corsages, leis, and making into perfume. *G. taitensis*, from the Society Islands, is a taller shrub with ovate leaves and white flowers with petals arranged in a pin-wheel fashion. It is popularly known as Tahitian Gardenia.

Both types are excellent for specimen, hedge, or pot planting. They thrive in full sun or light shade in well-drained soils with an acid reaction. Since plants are subject to attack by the rootknot nematode, it is advisable to sterilize or fumigate soil before planting. There are several commercial nematocides that give good control. Since the fumigants are poisonous, handle them with care and follow printed label directions to the letter.

PROPAGATING
Plants are quickly propagated from stem cuttings that are preferably about 6 or 7 inches long. Remove leaves from cuttings and dip ends in a rooting compound before placement in rooting media.

A gallon can in the shade containing vermiculite or some other clean media is suitable for rooting a limited number of cuttings. Wet the media thoroughly, insert the cuttings to about half their length, and cover with a plastic sheet. The covering serves to retard moisture evaporation, thus creating a humid atmosphere that is highly conducive to plant growth. Always replace cover over container following each application of water.

When cuttings have grown new shoots and strong roots, they may be removed for transplanting. Preferably, they should first be replanted into individual peat or paper pots before being transplanted into their permanent location. Fill peat pots with acidic, loose, fertile soil and plant rooted cuttings in them. Allow plants to grow up to root-bound stage before transplanting to permanent location.

Cuttings may also be rooted by immersing the butt ends about half their length in a glass container of tap water. Be sure to remove all leaves. A few of the terminal leaves may be left on tip cuttings. Change water regularly to prevent the formation of slime and rot organisms. When roots begin to appear, add a small amount of fertilizer to the water to hasten growth.

Leave the cuttings in water until strong roots and shoots have formed. They may then be transferred to paper pots for eventual transplanting to their permanent location. When rooting a large number of cuttings, it is advantageous to use a media for best success. Dip bottom ends in a hormone or rooting powder before inserting cuttings an inch apart in the propagation box. At the proper time, replant rooted cuttings in paper pots for eventual transfer to their permanent location.

GARDEN AND POT GROWING

Gardenias grow well out in the open either as specimen or hedge plants. For hedges, space plants no less than two feet apart in rows. Soil should be worked well down to at least the 15-inch depth. Gardenias may be kept strong and healthy with regular applications of water and fertilizer. Apply a complete garden fertilizer no less than once every other month. Moisture should be kept at a steady level.

Potted specimens should be planted in large containers filled with equal parts top soil and compost fortified with a small amount of general garden fertilizer. Gardenias grow quite rapidly, so large pots are most practical for container-grown specimens. Potted plants need to be fertilized more often than plants grown in the open.

Growers often forget the importance of soil acidity in growing Gardenias successfully. Soil should be tested periodically to be sure that the growing media is of the correct acidity (below pH 6.0).

Soils may be acidified by the addition of aluminum sulphate, iron sulphate, ammonium nitrate and sulfuric acid. Since iron sulphate is also a source of iron, it would be beneficial to use it where a chlorosis condition exists. Although sulphate takes some three months to bring about acidity in the soil, its effect is longer lasting. Sulfur requires bacterial action and moisture before it can be converted into sulfuric acid. Sulfur is economical, and one pound is sufficient to acidify about 100 sq. ft. of area.

With either aluminum sulphate, ammonium sulphate, or iron sulphate, use about one pound per 100 sq.ft. of area. However, six times as much aluminum sulphate is necessary to bring about the same pH change as for sulfur. The sulfates cause immediate reaction in the soil. To hasten acidification, work the material into the soil. Addition of large amounts of acid peat also brings about the necessary soil acidity ideal for Gardenia culture.

PESTS OF GARDENIA

Several insects, including aphids, mealy bugs, scale, white flies, and mites attack Gardenia. These pests can be controlled with spray applications of a general purpose pesticide mixed with a petroleum type spray oil. For best control, spray should cover the entire plant including leaves, stems and branches.

Aphids or plant lice are tiny insects and damage Gardenia by sucking sap from the buds, foliage, and the plant in general; they secrete honeydew on the leaves from which develops a black sooty mold. The substance is a fungus growth that injures the plant by shading and smothering the leaves.

Mealy Bugs congregate on leaves, stems, and flower buds in small groups and cover themselves and their eggs with a fluffy, white, cottony wax. Buds badly infested with the pests may drop before opening. Plants grown under dry conditions are often attacked by mites, which are difficult to detect with the naked eye. The insects remove chlorophyll, causing leaves to become pale green and stippled yellow. Heavy infestation is usually covered with a fine webbing.

Beetles are nocturnal feeders and usually hide during the day. The adults feed on foliage and the young larvae attack bark, roots, and underground stems. Infested plants are weakened as a consequence.

GINGER

The Ginger belongs to the *Zingiberaceae family*, which includes mostly tropical plants with large leaves and soft fleshy underground stems or rhizomes. The thick tuberous stems and vegetative parts are generally fragrant. The herbaceous plants are grown for their ornamental foliage, flowers, and fruit, or for conversion into spices, fiber, medicine, perfume and dye.

EDIBLE GINGER

The commercial or edible Ginger *(Zingiber officinale)* is the most valuable of known root spices. There are two types grown in Hawaii - Japanese and Chinese.

The Japanese variety produces short plants with small leaves and small rhizomes with a more pungent flavor than the Chinese. The Chinese variety is taller with larger leaves and larger rhizomes. The yield is also somewhat heavier, but the rhizomes are less pungent.

Edible Ginger grows best in soil that is acidic, loose, and well-drained but with high water-retention properties. Since the plants are susceptible to attack by nematodes and various soilborne diseases, it is essential to pre-treat the planting material and the planting soil. For soil treatment, consult your county agent.

For best insurance against diseases that may be carried in the planting material, always be sure to use only clean planting material taken from healthy plants. Sometimes planting material rots before sprouting. To prevent rot, dip it in a solution of berromyl and water (1 1/8 - 2 3/8 teaspoon per gallon of water). Seed pieces of rhizomes infected with root-knot nematode should be immersed in hot water (120° F) for about 10 minutes before planting. The hot water must be kept at a constant temperature, otherwise the treatment may not be effective.

Soil should be thoroughly cultivated to a depth of at least 12 inches before planting. If soil is poor, mix lots of decomposed organic matter in it. Furrows should be spaced about a foot apart. Place a small amount of general garden fertilizer in the bottom of the furrow, cover with about three inches of soil, and place the seed piece on top.

The planting material or rhizomes, each with three or four eyes, should be covered with about four inches of soil. Since Ginger demands a constant supply of moisture for steady growth, water should be applied regularly. One month after planting, apply another dose of general garden fertilizer at the rate of about 500 pounds per acre, or one heaping teaspoon per sq. ft. This application should be worked in about three inches deep and about eight inches away from the plants. At three months and at six months after planting, give plants separate doses of 800 pounds fertilizer per acre, or a heaping teaspoon per sq. ft. Work fertilizer into the soil about a foot away from the plants.

The crop matures with the appearance of flowers in about 8 or 10 months. Ginger for pickling should be harvested soon after flower production while the skin of the rhizomes is still tender. Ginger is mature enough for harvesting after plants have dried up. By then the rhizome skin has toughened suitably for storage. Never allow mature Ginger to remain more than 3 months in the ground, otherwise they will spoil with the formation of new growth. Immediately after the roots are dug up, they should be washed and air-dried in the shade for a couple of days to help heal cuts and bruises.

ORNAMENTAL GINGERS

Ornamental Gingers are commonly grown in the garden for their attractive flowers. They are propagated from sections of underground rhizomes. Since moisture is a primary factor in the cultivation of ornamental Ginger, see that plants always get sufficient water. Some varieties can grow with less moisture after plants become established.

Largest of the genus of Ginger is the *Alpinia*, of which the red and shell Gingers are the best known and most widely cultivated in Hawaii.

SHELL GINGER

The shell Ginger *(Alpinia nutans)* is a very ornamental plant native to eastern Asia. It produces open, foot-long flower clusters crowded with stiff, bell-shaped blossoms in white, yellow and red. Plants are from 6 to 12 feet in height with huge 2-foot long leaves about 6 inches wide. Plant propagating material in cultivated soil. Keep soil moist until shoots appear. After a good root system has developed, plants can stand less attention.

RED GINGER

Depending on the care given, red Ginger *(Alpinia purpurata)* plants may attain a height of from 4 to 10 feet. Native to the Pacific Islands, they are commonly grown in the home grounds because of their long flower spikes with numerous, open, brilliant red bracts and are very attractive. The flowering stems are popularly used in arrangements. New plants germinate from flower bracts and these may be used for propagation purposes. Planting material may also be obtained from sections of rhizomes of established clumps.

YELLOW GINGER

The Yellow Ginger *(Hedychium flavum Roxb.)* prefers wet soil and protection from strong winds. Native to India, the plant will grow in partial shade. During the flowering season, there appears an oval head of many highly perfumed light yellow blossoms, at the tips of the leafy stem.

WHITE GINGER

Flowers of the White Ginger *(Hedychium coronarum Koenig)* have a more pleasing fragrance than those of the Yellow Ginger. The blossoms are somewhat larger and are pure white in color; they are commonly strung into leis or produced into perfume.

KAHILI GINGER

The Kahili Ginger *(Hedychium gardnerianum Roscoe)* is native to the Himalaya mountains and, therefore, can withstand considerable cold. It is somewhat like the Yellow and White Gingers, and produces yellow, fragrant flowers. Long, oval heads of flowers resembling Hawaiian Kahilis are borne at the tips of stems.

TORCH GINGER

The Torch Ginger *(Phaeomeria magnifica)*, native to Indonesia, is a very large plant. Its leafy stems may rise over 10 feet in height with many large, alternate leaves in two rows. The flowers are very ornamental and develop into large, red or pink, cone-shaped heads. They are about a half foot long and produced on tall, erect stems separate from the leafy stems.

GUAVA

The Guava *(Psidium Guajava)* is found widely distributed in Hawaii from sea level up to 3,000 feet elevation. It is native to tropical America and was introduced to the islands sometime before 1800. The most common wild fruit in Hawaii, Guava can become a serious pest in cultivated areas and reservations.

Flowers of the Guava are white, perfect or bi-sexual, and occur in small clusters. The fruit ranges in size from small to large, with flesh varying in color from white to yellow to red, and may be either sweet or sour. It may be thick-fleshed with a few seeds in a small center cavity, or thin-fleshed with many seeds. Since flowers are produced on new wood, any practice that promotes vegetable growth will increase fruit productivity. The fruit has a high nutritive value and a very high vitamin C content. It may be eaten raw or processed into juices, jellies, and the like. Varieties with large fruit make excellent dessert.

Because of the increasing importance of Guava for processing, a program of selection and testing was initiated by the University of Hawaii. Scions and plants of superior types were also introduced from South Africa, Brazil, California and Florida, and seeds from the Philippines. These were graded according to their local performance on the basis of plant vigor and yield, fruit size, color, flavor and vitamin C content.

Many of the named horticultural varieties are dessert type Guavas, and are quite sweet and desirable for eating fresh. Very few, if any, of these may be found in local nurseries. However, many who appreciate sweet Guavas cultivate them in their gardens. The University of Hawaii has a collection of sweet types now under test. Anyone interested in growing a good variety for home production should keep a lookout for one or get information from his local county agent.

PROPAGATION

New plants can easily be grown from root cuttings measuring about six inches long and about 1/2 inch in diameter and imbedded in moist rooting media. Plants developed in this manner usually grow very slowly, and may take about a year to reach transplanting size. Plants may also be produced from roots severed from the mother plant. Roots to be severed should be at least two to three feet from the main trunk so as not to handicap the plant unduly. When plants are of good size, they may be dug up and transplanted to their permanent location.

Bud grafting has been found to be the quickest and most efficient method of propagating large numbers of plants. Stocks should be vigorous growing plants from 1/2 to 1 inch in diameter. Select a plump bud of the desired variety and insert it into an inverted T-cut in the bark of the stock plant. Wrap all the cut surface with budding tape or plastic material leaving the eye of the bud exposed. Prune off the tip of the stock plant to help force bud growth. The wrapping can be removed in three to eight weeks, depending on the rate of growth. However, make a point of removing the wrapping before the stock becomes constricted. A successful bud will be green and firmly in place.

PLANTING

Although Guava is quite hardy and will do well under most conditions, it would be to the advantage of the home gardener to plant it in a favorable spot. Select a location that receives plenty of sunshine and where it can be given ample water. If the soil is poor, add compost and manure, plus some fertilizer, to enrich it and improve drainage.

Dig the hole at least three times larger than the container of the plant. To minimize set back, transplanting is best done on a still, overcast day. Be sure that the roots are disturbed as little as possible. Remove a few of the lower leaves after the plant has been inserted in the hole. Leave a basin at the top and follow with a good irrigation of water. Although Guava should be spaced at least 15 feet apart in field planting, they may be planted closer in the home grounds, especially if space is a problem.

Since Guava begins branching when quite low, the home gardener must prune out all branches except the single main leader if he wants a tall tree. After the main trunk has grown to the desired height, the tree may be allowed to form five to eight strong well-spaced branches. Since the trees will produce smaller fruit with each passing year, it is desirable to cut back old branches to force out new growth from which larger fruit will be produced.

During the first year after transplanting, apply about a half pound of fertilizer at the base of the tree every three months. Follow this schedule and gradually increase the amount of plant food until the third year, when the tree should be receiving at least one pound of fertilizer each quarter. Use a good fruit tree fertilizer or one with a high amount of nitrogen.

PESTS OF GUAVA

Among the most destructive of insect pests of the Guava are fruit flies. The insects lay their eggs in the fruit and these hatch into maggots that burrow into maturing fruit.

Fruit flies may be controlled with sprays of an insecticide such as Malathion plus a sticking agent. For more effective control, include yeast hydrolysate as a bait for the flies. Spray at least twice a week, or until the flies have disappeared. Since flies will continue to lay their eggs in rotting fruit, be sure to gather all fallen fruit and bury them in the garden for composting.

Aphids and scales are not only a nuisance, but can cause considerable damage to Guava trees. These pests produce a secretion called "honeydew" that is sweetish and so attracts ants. A sooty mold fungus causing an unsightly black covering over foliage and fruit is also caused by the "honeydew." These insect pests can be controlled with a mixture of summer oil and nicotine sulfate. Spray at two-week intervals until the pests have been reduced in numbers.

Fruit may be picked when they develop a slight yellow tinge, depending on how they are to be used. For eating out of hand, the mature green stage is best.

A good fruiting tree will not only make a handsome specimen in the home grounds planting, but provide an almost year-round supply of delicious nutritious fruit. Because Guava grows easily and the fruit is so very useful, more home gardeners should include it in their plantings.

JADE VINE

One of the most spectacular, and undoubtedly among the most beautiful of the flowering vines introduced to Hawaii in the past couple of decades, is the Jade Vine *(Strongylodon macrobotrys)*. It is a native in the rain forests of the Philippines. It is a member of the Bean family *(Leguminosae)*, third largest family of flowering plants, which includes thousands of trees, shrubs, herbs and climbers widely distributed throughout the world and growing in various environments. More specifically, it belongs to the Pea subfamily *(Papilionatae)*.

It is a perennial, evergreen, woody, flowering plant whose stems are too weak to support itself in an upright position. Because of its growth habit, it may be grown for many purposes. It is useful for covering walls and fences, for decorating posts, as a screen, for covering arbors, pergolas and trellises, or trailing over the ground as a cover. It attaches itself to a support by twining its stems around the object.

The color of the blossoms is among the most unusual of flowering plants, being a most uncommon bluish jade-green. Blossoms are thick and soft, about two inches in length with long pointed, upturned keels. The blossoms hang in small clusters from a main flowering stalk that may be more than four feet long. Individual blossoms are long-lasting and sometimes strung into novel leis.

PROPAGATING
The plant may be propagated from seeds, cuttings or layerings. When seed is used, be sure that the material is fully ripe, but not so

old that it has lost its viability. Seeds may be planted preferably in a germination flat containing equal parts finely shredded tree fern fiber and vermiculite. Scatter the seeds evenly on the surface, press each down about 1/4 inch deep in the medium, and cover. Seeds may also be planted in shallow furrows and covered with about 1/4 inch of the growing media.

After planting, wet the media thoroughly and cover the surface with a plastic sheet with the ends secured to the bottom of the flat. This will not only keep the soil ideally warm, but lessen moisture evaporation. Place the germination flat in an out-of-the-way area and make sure it does not completely dry out. Depending on the season of the year, the seeds should germinate in 10 days to two weeks. After young seedlings poke through the surface, the plastic cover may be removed. Since the growing media is practically devoid of plant food, it is a good idea to include a small amount of general garden fertilizer with the irrigation water about once a week.

When the seedlings have passed the tender stage and begin to crowd each other, they are ready for transplanting. Individual seedlings should be transferred to paper or peat pots containing a mixture of equal parts of top soil, black sand and humus, plus a small amount of general garden fertilizer. Water flat well just before transplanting to facilitate lifting seedlings with a trowel or weeder. Give seedlings some shade and protection the first few days. When plants become nearly root-bound, they are ready for final transplanting.

Cuttings about 9 inches long taken from semi-woody stems are ideal for propagation. Remove leaves and dust lower ends with a rooting hormone powder before inserting them to about half their length in a mist propagation box. If a mist box is not available, use a propagation flat filled with equal parts of vermiculite and black sand. After inserting cuttings to the proper depth, water and cover with a plastic sheet. Keep media moist and when young shoots begin to appear, the plastic cover may be removed permanently. Plants may be allowed to become nearly root-bound before transplanting directly to a permanent location.

For layering purposes, select strong recumbent runners from an established plant. Cover one or two joints with a mound of soil three or four inches high. Keep mound moistened and in a few weeks, roots will begin to shoot from the node. Allow a strong root system to develop before severing the layered section from the mother plant. When the layer has recovered from the shock of separation, it may be transplanted to its permanent location.

Choose a cloudy day when transplanting layered plants. Give the plant a good watering before proceeding to lift it. Lift with a shovel and make sure that the root system is disturbed as little as possible. When the plant has been transferred to a previously prepared hole, strip off some of the lower leaves and apply water.

After the plant has been transferred to where it is to grow, some provision should be made for it to climb its support. A pole around which the elongating stems can twine themselves should be placed close to the plant and leading to the support, which may be a fence, arbor, pergola or tree trunk.

If the plant is to be trained as a screen against a bare wall, stout wire should be strung horizontally a foot apart close to the wall. Cross wires running vertically about two feet apart will help make a better screen. A wooden trellis may also be used.

The jade vine succeeds best in moist, rich soil with plenty of sunshine. However, if it is given a good start it may grow also under conditions somewhat less than ideal.

Before becoming established, plants may need some protection from insects. A good all-purpose insecticide plus a sticking agent will provide protection. Insects that could cause injury to the plant are aphids, mites, mealybugs and scales. Beetles, in both the larval and adult stages, also are potentially harmful because they chew on young plant tissue. Malathion spray applied according to directions on the label is generally an effective control.

Give plants sufficient moisture and applications of a general garden fertilizer twice a year and they should thrive. Plants that are strong and vigorous may need occasional pruning.

RED JADE

Another plant commonly known locally as the red jade vine is really *Mucuna bennettii*. It also is a member of the Bean family and endemic to New Guinea, where it is conspicuous along forested river banks. It is a striking creeping plant with glossy green, compound foliage borne on woody, twining stems. The highly attractive waxy flowers are brilliant scarlet, claw-like and shaped in the form of a sickle. The blossoms are carried in long pendant racemes from the axils. It is without doubt more spectacular than the blue Jade vine which it resembles, and came into popularity only the past several years. For the best display it should be trained into a support so the blossoms are conspicuous. It may be propagated by the same methods as used for the blue Jade vine. Cultural requirements are also nearly identical. It prefers moist rich soil in full sun.

LILIES

Commonly called aristocrats of the flower garden, Lilies are among the most beautiful and ornamental of bulb plants. They are of wide and varied geographical distribution, but may be found in greatest number in eastern Asia. Bulbs of the hardy types vary in size; some may be as small as marbles and others larger than baseballs. Some types grow no higher than two feet, while others may tower as much as 12 feet in height.

Lilies are without equal in their unique combination of beauty, gracefulness and stately magnificence. Contrary to popular opinion, they are quite easy to grow and adaptable to a wide range of conditions. In their natural habitats they grow under differing conditions of soil, climate, and environment. Most Lilies are robust, long-lived and of easy culture under various soil and climatic conditions.

WHERE TO PLANT

Since there is such a wide variety to choose from, suitable Lilies may be selected for almost any location or purpose. Most are excellent when grown in combination with other low-growing plants and shrubs, with their flowers rising above the foliage as they do in nature. With taller shrubs as a background of green, they may be shown off to good advantage, especially when in blossom. They also may be mass grown in borders or beds. Some of the more vigorous-growing and permanent types do well planted out in the open. There are, however, smaller dwarf types that are suitable for rock gardens or container gardening.

Some Lilies succeed best in full sun, but the majority require partial shade, as under the canopy of large trees. Flowers of sensitive varieties usually bleach under high light intensity.

Most types will thrive in light, well-drained soil containing high amounts of organic matter. However, there are a few that are partial to wet, swampy conditions. A few seem to prefer soil that is slightly alkaline, but most respond best to acid media. Fresh manure seems to be injurious as the material encourages bulb rot; as a result, only manure that has decomposed should be used. Bulbs are also sensitive to heat and need a mulch to keep them cool and to conserve moisture.

Light, water, temperature, and fertilizer, among other conditions, greatly influence the proper formation of buds and flowers. Poor light accompanied by high temperatures causes depletion of the supply of carbohydrates. A shortage of moisture causes buds to dry up and form abnormally. Too much fertilizer can injure and burn roots, thus interfering with their normal function which, in turn, reduces the amount of water supplied to the buds. Lack of Nitrogen may also interfere with normal development of flower buds.

Soil containing a high amount of Phosphate seems to retard growth. Plants will benefit from soil containing moderate amounts of commercial plant food, but excessive fertilizer applications tend to injure the developing root system. This causes dwarfing of later growth and a reduction in flower production.

Newly started plants, especially those grown in pots, need a steady, moderate supply of Nitrogen fertilizer for best growth. This may be efficiently and conveniently applied with the irrigation water.

THE EASTER LILY

The most valuable species for florist production is the Easter Lily *(L. longiflorum)* of which the Japanese, Bermuda and American varieties are the most important. Flowers are large, white, fragrant and trumpet-shaped. As a potted plant, it is especially adapted for church, wedding and other occasions, and as a cut flower is very useful for design work.

For growing out in the open or in containers, Easter Lilies are excellent and may be grown practically the year round. The unique form of their plants and flowers may be used to lend an elegance and beauty all their own.

PROPAGATION

Lilies may be propagated from seeds, scales, stem bulblets or by natural increase of the bulbs. Since Easter Lilies do not breed true, they are most commonly propagated by vegetative means.

If seeds are used, sow them in a seedling flat containing a fine planting media. Bulbs should be planted immediately after harvest for best results. Injury and drying from exposure are detrimental to bulb growth. Bulbs are most easily grown in moderate amount of complete fertilizer high in phosphate and potash. Generous irrigation is preferred, and field-grown plants should never be allowed to dry out completely. Container-grown specimens thrive excellently in fertile soil with much water.

For the garden, bulbs may be planted 18 inches apart and covered with about four inches of soil during the cold months, and as deep as six inches in warm weather. Bulbs may be held in cold storage to force slower production at selected or pre-determined periods. For this purpose, they should be refrigerated at about 32 degrees Fahrenheit for at least six weeks, after which they may be planted. Bulbs have been kept in cold storage for nearly five months without apparent bad effect.

Potted lilies are ready for display or exhibit when the first flower is fully open. As cut flowers, the stems or flower heads should be cut the day before they fully open. To prevent discoloration of the perianth, the stamens may be removed.

When bulbs fail to grow or develop unevenly, they have either been prematurely dug, improperly stored, or watered unevenly.

PESTS AND DISEASES

A disease that begins as small elongated or circular spots that eventually occupy the entire leaf, causing eventual rotting of the crown, is due to high humidity. Good air circulation will minimize the incidence of the disease. Control may be brought about by spraying with a Bordeaux mixture formulated by mixing 1 pound copper sulfate and 1 pound lime in 12 gallons of water.

Plant die-back characterized by discolored, curled leaves and bunchy tops is due to nematode infestation. Nematode attack can be controlled by treating bulbs with hot water and formaldehyde, and fumigating the growing media with a nematocide before planting. Infected plants should be destroyed to prevent spread.

Untreated bulbs are also a source of a virus that causes leaves to speckle and streak, resulting in stunted growth. Since aphids spread the virus, the pests should be controlled with a good, all-purpose insecticide. Splitting of buds is also caused by injury from aphids. Mites also cause some injury and should be controlled with a combined insecticide-miticide.

Follow a good sanitation program coupled with approved cultural practices to minimize production problems.

LYCHEE

The Lychee *(Litchi chinensis)* produces a most attractive and delicious fruit, and is a medium-sized tree that is highly suitable for backyard planting or home grounds landscaping. The red, rough-skinned fruit contains a white pulp that is juicy and sweet.

The tree has a broad crown of thick foliage that makes a nice shade. The Lychee is native to southern China where it has been in cultivation for more than 20 centuries. It was introduced to Hawaii in 1873 and first planted near the corner of School and Nuuanu Streets in Honolulu.

The Lychee may be found growing on all the major islands, from sea level up to a 3,000 foot elevation. Most of the varieties grown in Hawaii have been imported from China or Florida. They can be differentiated by size of leaves and length of petioles; shape, color and size of fruits.

Among the most consistent producers of all varieties in Hawaii is the Groff, which was developed locally. Its dull-red fruit is comparatively small and contains tiny seeds. Clusters contain more than 20 fruit each.

The Lychee will grow in most types of soils, but seems to prefer rich loams with a slightly acid reaction. It does best in full sun, but can withstand some shade. Because of its brittle wood, the Lychee needs protection from strong winds. For favorable results in the home grounds, it should be planted on the leeward side of the house.

PROPAGATION

Plants can be grown from seed but normally take longer before producing fruit, and these are usually of poor quality. Grafting may be used to propagate plants but is not a popular practice. The most common method of propagation is by air-layering. Plants produced in this manner are identical with the parent, and also are known to produce fruit earlier.

To accomplish the operation, select a branch about 1/2 inch thick of the desired variety. Be sure that the branch is in a convenient working position. Scrape off about a 3/4 inch ring of bark from the branch. The girdled area is then wrapped with moist sphagnum moss encased in a durable sheet of plastic. The top and bottom ends of the plastic covering are secured with string, raffia or some other convenient material.

Roots will form in two or three months and can be seen through the plastic. After a good root system has developed, the branch should be sheared off at the lower end from the main plant. The plastic casing should be carefully removed so as not to disturb the roots and the branch planted in a container, such as a gallon can. Remove most of the lower leaves to reduce shock or set-back. The new plant should be left in the shade until it shows signs of recovery. It should then be exposed to full sun for a few hours each day until it has become accustomed to its new environment.

TRANSPLANTING

Only after the plant has become well-established in the container should it be transplanted to its permanent location. For backyard planting, trees may be spaced about 20 feet apart with some protection from the house or other trees. For orchards, plants should be grown at least 25 feet apart in rows.

Since the Lychee is very sensitive, it should preferably be transplanted on a cloudy day in soil that is wet. Prepare the hole before transplanting by digging it three times as wide and at least twice as deep as the container holding the plant. Fill the hole with rich top soil containing much organic matter. It is advisable to mix a small amount of superphosphate and fruit tree fertilizers with soil before actual transplanting.

While still in the container, the plant should be given a good watering to simplify removal. If the plant does not come out of the container easily, tap it lightly with a hammer handle. Do this until the plant slips easily from the can. If the operation is done correctly, the soil ball will remain intact with little or no disturbance to the plant roots.

Place the plant in the hole making sure that it is in about the same level as it was in the can. After the hole has been refilled with soil, give the plant a good soaking. Give the plant some protection and keep the soil moist until it begins to show signs of growth.

FERTILIZING

For the first year, about 1/4 to 1/2 pound of fruit tree fertilizer should be applied at four month intervals. The fertilizer should be cultivated into the surface and followed with a good watering. Increase the dose slightly for the same interval in the second year. The rate should be increased to a pound per application every four months in the third year. For the fourth year, double the rate for the previous year. Thereafter, applications should be at least one pound of fertilizer for each diameter inch of trunk.

Old or mature trees can best be fertilized by means of holes dug beneath the dripline. Spaced about 18 inches apart, holes about an inch in diameter and some six inches deep should ring the dripline, be cultivated into the surface, and followed with a good watering. These holes can be made quite easily with a soil augur or the pointed end of a pickax.

Place the required amount of fertilizer in each hole and follow with water before covering with soil. Increase the dose slightly for the same interval in the second year. The rate should be increased to a pound per application every four months in the third year. Thereafter, applications should be at least one pound of fertilizer for each diameter inch of trunk. Fertilizer applied in this manner is close to the feeder roots, and consequently is made use of immediately by the tree. This method of application, although a bit more time consuming, is more efficient and, in the long run, more economical.

Much guesswork in fertilization is eliminated when the soil is sampled and analyzed. For this service, consult your local Extension County Agent.

PRUNING AND GIRDLING

A young tree usually has a habit of sending out many branches. All side branches should be removed in favor of a single main leader. When the tree has grown to the proper height, it may be allowed to develop more naturally. However, weak or crooked branches should be pruned off and the tree allowed to grow into the desired shape. Pruning may be done whenever convenient, preferably before the branches have become too large.

Most varieties of Lychee, except the Groff, need to be girdled to promote fruit production. The ideal time to do this is the middle of September. In general, Hawaiian conditions are too wet during the period when the trees should be dormant. As a result of the moisture, they flush out into new vegetative growth. Girdling suppresses the formation of new leaves and causes the accumulation of carbohydrates above the girdle. The result is the production of flowers.

Girdling is an age-old practice whereby a strip of bark encircling the branch or trunk is completely removed. This is best accomplished with a light pruning saw. Run the saw around the trunk and remove about 1/6 inch strip of bark. Be careful, as an unusually wide girdle can cause the death of the branch or tree.

Although the whole tree may be girdled at once, this is not recommended since the strain could cause injury. A preferable practice is to girdle only half of the tree each year. This practice results in less shock to the tree.

INSECTS

Erinose mites, several kinds of scales, and beetles, are among the most troublesome pests.

Mites cause unsightly galling of the under surface of leaves. For best control, spraying should be done before new leaves form. Use a spray containing a mixture of one to two pounds of wettable sulphur in 20 gallons or 2 1/2 tablespoons per gallon of water.

Scale infestations can be checked with bi-weekly sprays of Malathion.

Chinese rose beetles, if left unchecked, can practically defoliate young trees. Insecticides should be sprayed around the base of the tree where beetles hide during the day. Do not apply to foliage.

MANGO

The Mango *(Mangifera indica)*, native to India and adjacent countries, is one of the finest and best known of tropical fruits. Consequently, it is sometimes called "the king of fruits." It was introduced to Hawaii sometime after 1800.

Reputed as the most popular fruit tree in the state, the Mango is grown on all of the major islands. It thrives best at low elevations up to 1,000 feet but specimens may be found growing as high as 3,000 feet. The pointed ovoid fruit is attractive at maturity and, depending on variety, ranges from patches of dark red or purplish to golden yellow in color.

A Mango tree may grow as high as 70 feet covered with heavy luxuriant foliage. It makes a handsome addition to the home landscape, providing both delicious fruit and shade. It is hardy, after becoming established, and will tolerate drought and poor soil. Although it is easily grown, it cannot stand poor drainage conditions. The Mango will grow in most types of soils, but succeeds best in fertile soils in hot, dry areas.

The most widely grown Mango variety in the islands is Hayden, which was introduced from Florida. Next in popularity is Pirie, a variety from India. Although there have been a few outstanding Hawaiian seedlings, most other named varieties grown in the islands come from Florida.

The Mango is sensitive to the care it receives, and will respond well to good cultural practices. For more detailed information on varieties suitable to your area, consult your local Extension County Agent or your nurseryman.

FROM SEED AND GRAFTS

Since most Mangos do not reproduce true from seed, they are usually propagated by grafting. However, some Mango types such as the Chinese, Shibata and a few others, will reproduce true from seed.

For the best results, graft pencil-thick scions onto vigorous growing stock. The Mango can be grafted in several ways, but use the method with which you're most familiar. Propagating by air-layering is not recommended.

In selecting a tree for planting, choose the variety suited to your conditions. Be sure that the graft union has completely healed before it is transplanted. Since the tree will occupy a lot of space when fully grown, give it ample room. A spacing of at least 35 feet between rows is good.

TRANSPLANTING

Before transplanting, the soil should be wetted down thoroughly to facilitate digging operations. Prepare the hole at least three times as wide and two times as deep as the container in which the plant is growing. A larger hole is preferable. Fill the hole with fertile soil containing a high amount of organic matter. Enrich the mixture with a small amount of general garden or fruit tree fertilizer.

Soak the can in which the tree is growing to facilitate removal. Tap the can on the side and the tree will separate from the container without too much difficulty. Be sure to keep as much of the soil as possible intact with the roots to reduce chances of setback. Plant the tree in the prepared hole at the same level as it was in the container.

Following transplanting, the tree should receive a good soaking of water. The tree should be provided with some kind of protection to prevent drying for the first few days after transplanting. Depending on the amount of rainfall, the tree should be irrigated at least once a week to insure steady growth.

FERTILIZING

Four months after transplanting, the tree should receive at least a quarter pound of general garden or fruit tree fertilizer. For quick action, the fertilizer should be worked into the soil surface, being careful not to disturb the young roots. This should be followed by irrigation.

To keep the tree growing at its best, it should receive a half pound of general garden or fruit tree fertilizer every four months after it is eight months old. Keep this up until the tree is two years old. Thereafter, it should receive at least one semiannual application of one to two pounds of general garden or fruit tree fertilizer until the end of the fourth year. Double the dose after the fifth year.

Older trees should receive one to two pounds of general garden or fruit tree fertilizer for every inch diameter of trunk. This should be applied at flowering time and again after the last fruit has been picked. For best effect with mature trees, the fertilizer should be placed in holes following the drip line. The holes measuring at least one inch in diameter and some six inches deep, dug about 18 inches apart, can be made with a soil augur or similar instrument. The pointed end of a pickaxe may also be used.

Divide the total amount of fertilizer by the number of holes for even distribution. Place the fertilizer in the holes, add water, cover with soil. It is wise to remember that fertilizer cannot take effect unless it is accompanied by moisture.

The Mango grows best in full sun, but needs some protection from wind if it is to produce heavy crops. Trees grown in the backyard are afforded protection by houses and buildings nearby.

DISEASES AND INSECTS

Rainy weather accompanying the flowering season can seriously reduce fruit yields because of the high incidence of anthracnose disease. One of the most serious Mango diseases, anthracnose causes flowers to turn black and fruit to drop prematurely. In localities of heavy precipitation, it is advisable to plant varieties resistant to the disease, such as Fairchild. Anthracnose is not commonly found in areas of low rainfall.

In dry areas, tips of leaves may be burned or discolored. This can be corrected by irrigation at more frequent intervals, or by the application of fruit tree fertilizer fortified with higher amounts of potash fertilizer. However, to be on the safe side, take a soil sample. Have it analyzed to see if the soil is deficient in potassium, and be guided accordingly.

Among the most damaging pests of the Mango fruit is the oriental fruit fly. A weekly spray of Malathion will give relief. Apply the spray to the tree and also to adjacent shrubs, which might provide sanctuary for adult flies.

To control aphids, mites, scales, and thrips, an insecticide spray may be used up to 7 days before harvest. Do not spray during blooming season.

By controlling scales, problems with sooty mold can be eliminated.

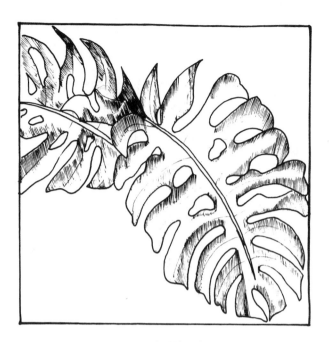

MONSTERA

One of the most popular climbing foliage ornamentals in Hawaii is the Monstera *(Monstera deliciosa)*, which is widely used both indoors and out. It is among more than 100 genera that belong to the Arum family *(Aracae)*. A large evergreen vine, it is one of some 30 species commonly found in tropical America, Mexico, and Costa Rica.

The large, thick, leathery, hhe can on the side and the tree will separate from the container without too much difficulty. Be sure to keep as much of the soil as possible intact with the roots to reduce chances of setback. Plant the tree in the prepared hole at the same level as it was in the container.

Following transplanting, the tree should receive a good soaking of water. The tree should be provided with some kind of protection to prevent drying for the first few days after transplanting. Depending on the amount of eart-shaped, glossy green leaves are perforated and lobed when mature, may be nearly a yard in length, and selected foliage is often sprayed for Christmas decorations. Although Monstera is cultivated chiefly for its large, such as tree trunks. It prefers moist, shady locations but is adaptable and hardy to both dry and rather cold areas. Although native to the tropics, it surprisingly can withstand near freezing temperatures.

INDOOR PLANTS

Monstera is most commonly grown in containers and as such used for indoor display. It may be grown directly in fancy vases or large pots placed inside an urn. Trained on a totem pole, it is quite handsome and may be left indoors for a long time without any seeming adverse effect.

Specimens intended for placement indoors should be taken out occasionally for cleansing and spraying with pesticides. When this is done, they should not be left too long in the sun, otherwise they will burn.

Another media that is commonly used in which to grow Monstera is plain water. Immerse the cutting in a container with at least one node below the water level. The cutting will show no signs of setback as it continues to absorb moisture and eventually sprout roots at the joint. However, if the plant is to remain in water for any length of time, it is advisable to dissolve in small amount of fertilizer when the water is changed at regular intervals. A water-cultured plant may be potted or transplanted elsewhere at any time.

PROPAGATION

Because of its relative ease of growth, Monstera may be propagated successfully in a number of ways. All of the known methods of propagation including air or ground layering can be used with success but since these operations take time, are seldom used.

The most popular method of propagation is root cuttings. Cuttings may be of any convenient length, depending on the purpose and supply. These should have at least one or, preferably, two nodes. Cuttings may be taken from any section of the plant and will grow. However, old woody material may take longer to sprout shoots. Tip cuttings and those taken close to the growing point usually are more satisfactory.

To lessen incidence of mortality, cuttings should be dusted with a rooting hormone powder before placement in the propagation flat. Any remaining foliage should be clipped off. For tip cuttings, remove all leaves except one or two at the growing point.

Cuttings should preferably be imbedded horizontally and covered with about 1/4 inch of the growing media. Place flat in a corner of the garden and keep moist until shoots emerge, after which less water may be applied.

Cuttings can also be rooted by placing them on the ground surface in a shady corner of the garden and covering with moist soil or wood shavings. So long as they are kept moist, cuttings will continue to grow and may be lifted for transplanting.

CONTAINER CULTURE

For container culture and display purposes, plant two started cuttings in a large pot with loamy, well-drained soil. Two plants will produce much more foliage than only one and will, therefore, be more attractive. In the early stages, before the plants start vining, they will not need any support. When stems begin to get too long, they may be trained on a totem pole, two or three feet tall, imbedded in the middle of the container. If the pole is not used, as an alternative, the elongating stems may be entwined around each other to form a globe of foliage. Eventually, however, the plant will appear untidy and may need to be pruned back to restore its neat appearance. Also, they may need to be repotted.

Repotting is a good time to do some root pruning. Don't hesitate to trim a good portion of the roots, as new and stronger roots will develop where the others were removed. Aerial roots may be removed without any adverse effect.

OUTDOOR CULTURE

In outdoor culture, Monstera may be grown and trained to climb building walls, fences or trees. Against a bare wall, the huge, handsome foliage breaks the monotony and lends an indescribably beautiful appearance. The strong roots anchor the plant securely, making it almost impossible to dislodge.

Monstera is excellent for training on large trees with tall, bare trunks. They seem to be at home under such an environment of shade and humidity. Their foliage becomes nice and green with no browning, like those from specimens exposed to searing sun. Under conditions simulating its natural habitat, Monstera grows at its best and produces huge overlapping leaves.

After establishment, Monsteras require very little maintenance except occasional watering and, in very poor soils, an infrequent application of general garden fertilizer is recommended.

So long as plants are kept growing vigorously, they are seldom bothered by pests. Once in a while, a plant may show evidence of rotting at the base. This is due either to use of diseased plant material or soilborne organisms. When this occurs, sever the plant just above the rotting section and repot in fresh, clean soil.

Sometimes young, growing leaves become distorted and wrinkled because of injury by thrips. The lower side of the foliage becomes streaked with gray and is specked with tiny brownish black dots, which are actually excretions of the thrips. Malathion applied according to directions on the label is effective control.

OLEANDER

The Oleander *(Nerium oleander)*, a member of the Periwinkle family, is poisonous but extensively used for home grounds planting. Its scientific name is derived from Neros, meaning humid, and refers to the kind of place in which the shrub thrives.

The ornamental plant, native to southern Europe and Persia, is an evergreen. Its leathery leaves are lanceolate and deep green in color, and produced in whorls of three. The flowers are funnel-shaped and may be single, semi-double or double, ranging in color from white to crimson. The blossoms are unscented and borne in clusters at the tips of shoots. Flowers are produced on new growth. All parts of the plant including flowers, foliage, bark, root, wood and sap are poisonous. However, the milky juice, when used in small amounts, is said to have some medicinal value.

The tender flowering shrub may grow as high as 20 feet. It is rapid-growing and may be used for specimen, mass and hedge planting. Although seldom used as a pot plant in Hawaii, Oleander is excellent for container cultivation.

The Oleander succeeds best in fertile, well-drained soil. However, it also is quite hardy and manages to survive in a surprising variety of soil conditions. Once established, Oleander will grow in soils ranging from sandy to clay as long as it receives ample moisture. It is partial to sunny locations where it will be most floriferous, but will grow in partial shade. Shady conditions encourage leggy growth, but discourage flower production.

PROPAGATION

The most extensively used and most practical means of propagation is by cuttings. Woody cuttings, except extremely young soft growth at branch tips, are best. Cuttings may be divided into convenient sections from 9 to 12 inches long. These may be rooted in many ways - in a germination flat, a mist propagation box, in water, individual containers, or planted directly in place.

When starting cuttings in a germination flat, use clean black sand that is always kept moist. The cuttings should be stripped of all foliage and imbedded at an angle. Insert them about 5 inches deep and an inch apart. Place the flat in partial shade until shoots appear, when it may be given more light. After shoots appear, water with soluble fertilizer to promote growth. When cuttings have developed strong roots, they are ready for transplanting. Transplanting is best done in the late afternoon or on a cloudy day. Remove the new plants carefully from the propagation flat, making sure that the root system is not damaged. Follow transplanting with a good irrigation.

A big advantage for rooting cuttings in individual paper pots is the absence of setback when transplanting. The pots are filled with rooting media and a single cutting is inserted in each. The cuttings are cared for in much the same manner as those started in germination flats. The plants are ready for transplanting after growth of strong roots. The plants with their pots intact are transferred to their new location. The roots of the plants will penetrate through the paper, which eventually will decompose.

Another convenient method for starting cuttings is to place them in a container of water. The cuttings should be immersed in about four inches of water. Although cans may be used for this purpose, a transparent glass jar through which emerging roots are visible is better. The water should be changed regularly to discourage growth of algae and rot organisms. After roots have started, a small amount of fertilizer may be added to the water to hasten growth.

WHERE USED

Oleander make nice specimen or group plantings. However, they are most commonly used for hedges. They make a good, thick hedge for privacy purposes, or as protection or windbreak for other plants.

For hedges, plants may be grown about a foot apart in single rows. If a thick hedge is desired, plants may be spaced closer in single rows or grown in double rows. Since hedges are more or less permanent plantings, it is advantageous to grow them in soil that has been well worked. If the soil is poor and does not drain well, improve it by mixing coarse material and much compost, to which a small amount of general garden fertilizer has been added.

For the first few weeks after planting, water the hedge thoroughly. To be sure that plants are receiving water in the deep root zone, furrow irrigation is advisable. Make an irrigation furrow to one side of the hedge row. For double row plantings, make the furrow in between. Water from a hose may then be applied in the furrows. Apply sufficient water to wet soil to a depth of at least 10 to 20 inches. Deep watering encourages development of a deep root system that helps sustain plants through a period of drought.

PRUNING AND FEEDING

When plants are about two feet high, they should be given a light pruning to encourage development of side branches. This practice helps produce bushy plants. A second pruning at the four-foot height will encourage additional branching that should insure a good, thick hedge when the plants are given their final pruning at the legal six-foot height.

When plants spread out too far from the hedge row, they may be given a side pruning to help confine their growth. Since Oleander is toxic, use care when handling branch trimmings. The cuttings should never be left lying around where children can accidentally get at them. Bundle them up for the garbage man to truck away to the incinerator.

Very old hedges sometimes become ragged and thin. They can be rejuvenated to produce the desired cover by being pruned close to the ground. They soon produce a wealth of shoots that grow into a thick cover of foliage.

Established hedges may be fertilized to advantage at least twice a year. Use a general garden fertilizer or else have your soil tested so plant nutrients can be applied in the required amounts. The fertilizer may be cultivated into the surface inch of soil and watered. It also may be applied with the irrigation water. For old hedges with extensive roots, the fertilizer is best applied in 8-inch deep holes spaced about 18 inches apart and about 24 inches from the hedge row. Remember that plants can only take advantage of fertilizer when there is moisture present. So do not forget to water after fertilizer has been applied.

Oleander is remarkably free of insects and diseases as its toxic properties seem to be helpful in keeping it pest-free. At the first signs of pest attack, spray with a good insecticidal mixture.

PAPAYA

The Papaya *(Carica papaya)* is a giant herbaceous plant with a hollow trunk native to tropical America. Its large, broad, deeply-lobed leaves are clustered at the top of the trunk or tips of branches. It produces melon-like fruit that differs greatly in size, shape, and color. The fruit is an economical source of Vitamin A and Vitamin C. Ascorbic acid content increases as the fruit ripens.

Papaya was introduced to Hawaii sometime before 1823. Among the many varieties grown, the Solo, imported in 1919, is the most popular. The Solo variety has been much improved through selection. It produces three types of trees - (a) hermaphrodite, (b) female, and (c) male. Hermaphrodite or bisexual trees produce large, perfect flowers that have both stamens and a pistil. The fruit is elongated, pear-shaped and slightly ridged.

Female or unisexual trees bear large, imperfect flowers with a pistil but no stamen. These flowers need to be pollinated before they can produce fruit. The fruit is characteristically somewhat roundish in shape. Male trees produce small, imperfect flowers with stamens but no pistil. They seldom produce fruit, but, if they do, they are elongated.

WHERE TO PLANT

Fertile, well-drained soil high in organic matter is best for Papaya culture. Since the plant grows rapidly, it needs a steady supply of fertilizer or plant nutrients and moisture if it is expected to do its best.

Sunny areas in the lowlands, with protection from strong gusts of wind, are ideal growing locations. Adverse conditions such as reduced sunlight, insufficient fertilizer, strong winds and drought all hinder proper development of foliage, which in turn greatly affects the quality and quantity of fruit.

The root system of Papaya is somewhat delicate, and can be easily injured by cultivation or if subjected to waterlogged conditions. Poorly drained soils are not well-aerated and, thus, can cause root rot and, oftentimes, even death to the tree.

PROPAGATION

Plants are propagated from seeds of ripe fruit selected from high producing trees. The seeds are usually allowed to dry before planting. However, seeds taken directly from the fruit also may be planted immediately in soil. Seeds may be sown in flats, small tin cans, peat pots or other convenient containers.

Soil for starting seeds should be a mixture of equal parts of clean top soil, compost and cinders. Plant four or five seeds in each tin can or paper pot and cover with about one inch of soil and keep moist. Seeds germinate in a few days and seedlings may be allowed to grow in the containers until they have three or four true leaves. At this stage, remove all seedlings except the two strongest plants.

TRANSPLANTING

When the seedlings are several inches high, or have developed a good root system, they are ready for transplanting. Seedlings should be planted in holes spaced about eight feet apart. The planting holes should be at least 15 inches in width and about a foot in depth. If soil is poor, it should be fortified with generous amounts of humus or compost and a handful of general garden or fruit tree fertilizer. Heavy clay soil that drains poorly can be improved with the addition of large amounts of manure, compost and cinders. On the other hand, sandy soil can be improved to better retain moisture by mixing it with generous quantities of manure, compost and humus.

Seedling plants will separate from their tin containers readily if they are first soaked in water before transplanting. Seedlings grown in paper or cardboard cups such as peat pots do not need to be removed from their containers, and may be planted directly into holes.

A recommended practice is to plant two seedlings about six inches apart in each hole. Plant them a little lower than they were in their containers. Place a small amount of general garden or fruit tree fertilizer several inches below the seedling roots and cover with soil. The seedlings should then be resting several inches above this band of fertilizer. Soil is then packed against the newly-transplanted seedlings. A small amount of general garden or fruit tree fertilizer is spread on the surface in a circle about five inches from the seedlings. The seedlings should be given a good soaking of water after transplanting.

If the operation has been correctly done and without much disturbance to the plant root system, there should be no setback. The plants should pick up and grow rapidly with ample nutrients within easy reach of their spreading root system.

After about five months, when plants have started to blossom, the type of flowers can be distinguished. The better of two trees that produces perfect or hermaphrodite flowers should be allowed to remain in the hole. The other should be removed. If both trees produce either female or male flowers, they should be both removed and replaced with one that produces perfect flowers.

FERTILIZING

To keep trees growing rapidly and vigorously, apply about a pound of fruit tree fertilizer when the tree is about six months old, in a shallow trench about two feet away and surrounding it. Water the fertilizer before covering the trench with soil. When the tree is about a year old and has begun producing mature fruit, give it another dose of one pound of fertilizer applied in the same manner as previously. Thereafter, fertilizer applications should be about one pound every three months. Given ample plant food in the form of complete fruit tree fertilizer and regular watering, Papaya will produce at its best.

Fruit should be picked when tinges of yellow appear or when half yellow. If left to ripen on the tree, fruit is often damaged by fruit flies and birds.

Unfruitfulness in Papaya may be either due to inherited characteristics or improper cultural practices or pests. Insufficient water, or lack of it coupled with inadequate amounts of plant food or fertilizer, can cause Papaya to fruit irregularly or fail to fruit at all. Tight soils with improper aeration or those that drain poorly are also causes of poor fruit production or death to trees.

During the hot summer months, some forms of hermaphroditic trees may go sterile when pistils fail to develop properly. This causes alternate periods of fruitfulness and barrenness. Trees that are either female or male do not fruit regularly.

INSECTS

Papaya may be affected by root pests commonly found in improperly drained soils, and by stem and leaf diseases, which also can cause plant decline. Insect and mite damage to foliage can also cause Papaya to fruit irregularly.

Some chemicals such as oil sprays, Bordeaux Mixture and weed killers, can cause injury to foliage resulting in tree decline and fruit failure. Papaya growing under shade or in nematode-infested soil will not produce fruit regularly. A combination spray mixture of Malathion and sulphur will control most insect pests, including mites.

Papaya trees kept healthy and vigorous with regular care will provide fruit for a surprisingly long time.

PASSION FRUIT

One of the most useful vines for home grounds planting is the Passion fruit, which inspired the early Spaniards to give it a distinctive common name because of its unusual flowers. Of the six varieties that fruit in Hawaii, the most common are the purple Passion fruit *(Passiflora edulis)* and the yellow Passion fruit *(Passiflora edulis, flavicarpa)*.

Native to Brazil, the purple variety was introduced to Hawaii from Australia sometime in 1880 and first planted in the district of Lilikoi in East Maui, from which it received its Hawaiian name. The larger yellow Passion fruit, commonly grown commercially, was introduced by the Hawaii Agricultural Experiment Station in 1923. It originated as a sport in Australia and contains a higher percentage of juice and acid than the purple variety.

The purple Passion fruit is better suited than the yellow variety to growing at higher elevations. Fruits are smaller, but they possess better flavor and aroma, either fresh or processed. The yellow Passion fruit grows well at low elevations, ranging from sea level to 2,500 feet. It grows more vigorously and produces more fruit than the purple variety. In both varieties, fruit falls to the ground when mature.

Flowers of the purple variety open at dawn and close before noon, while those of the yellow variety open about noon and close before midnight. Because of this flowering pattern, there is very little crossing between the two types.

Any gardener who is observant and wants only vigorous high producing plants can achieve his goal through a plant selection program. Plants that produce fruit with orange-colored skin should be discarded as these are usually off-flavor and have a woody taste. Vines that bear round fruit are not as productive as those with oval fruit.

PROPAGATION

Although Passion fruit may be propagated from seed, the home gardener wishing to grow plants with proven productivity can best accomplish his objective by using cuttings or air layers of the selected plants. Seed of ripe fruit may be planted immediately in a seedling flat. Germination begins in about two weeks, but some seeds may take as long as three months before emerging from the ground.

When seedlings have two sets of true leaves, they should be transplanted into paper cups or peat pots. They should remain in their containers until they have developed a good root system, after which they can be planted (pots and all) in their permanent location. Propagation material for cutting or air-layering should be selected only when vines show signs of active growth.

Stems that are either too old or immature are unsuitable for cuttings. The best cutting material is secured from the section between the topmost mature leaf and down to the fully extended branch. Cuttings should be severed close to the nodes and not have more than three nodes each. The cuttings may be rooted in moist sawdust, wood shavings, black sand, vermiculite or some other clean propagating material. The lower two thirds of the cuttings should be imbedded in the propagating medium. They will form roots in about a month, and may be transferred to paper or peat pots after there are signs of active growth. Keep them in the containers till they have developed a good root system, after which they may be transplanted to their permanent location.

In air-layering, select woody stems that are in a convenient working position. Scrape off a ring of bark about 3/4 inch in width and wrap the section with moist sphagnum moss encased in a sheet of plastic. Tie the top and bottom ends of the plastic sheet with raffia or strong twine. When a strong root system has formed, which will be visible through the plastic sheet, sever off the lower end of the branch from the mother plant. The plastic wrapping should be carefully removed with least disturbance to the root system, and the new plant planted in a convenient container. Remove some of the old leaves and place the new plant under shade for a few days, being sure to keep it watered. When the plant has shown signs of growth, transplant it to its permanent location.

Propagating by air-layering is advantageous in that it gives the grower a plant with good growth in a relatively short time. In other words, there is a considerable saving in growing time.

WHERE TO GROW

Passion fruit may be used to good advantage for decorating when growing against a wall or fence, to provide shade when growing on an arbour, or as a ground cover for areas that are difficult to maintain. The vine is quite versatile and may be trained into many forms of growth.

The plant is quite hardy and will do surprisingly well in many soils. A prime requirement is that the soil be well-drained. Although it thrives with ample moisture, the vine cannot withstand waterlogging for very long.

For planting in rows, Passion fruit should be placed at least eight feet apart. If they are to be grown on trellises, the top wire should be at least 6 or 7 feet from the ground. This height facilitates cultural and harvesting operations, and is more favorable to maximum vine growth because of the greater exposure to sun.

New vines should be planted in holes at least 18 inches wide and 18 inches deep. Soil that is fertile and loose, to which some fertilizer had been added, is best. Leave a small depression at the top of the planting hole to retain water when irrigating.

FERTILIZING

Apply a pound of fertilizer such as 10-5-20 to each plant six months after planting, and follow this with a similar dose at the end of the first year. Plants that are vigorous will produce strong vines with a proportionately larger yield of fruit.

Soils that are strongly acidic should receive some lime to tone down their acidity. To be on the safe side, take a soil sample and have it analyzed. Recommendations on kinds and amounts of fertilizer and lime to apply will follow the analysis. Generally, a fertilizer with moderate nitrogen, low phosphate and high potash is best. Ask your local county agent for assistance in soil sampling.

After the plant has spread out to some extent, it may be necessary to prune it for convenience. Prune only as little as is needed, since any excess removal of branches and vines can severely affect plant growth and productivity.

PEST CONTROL

The control of insect pests that attack Passion fruit is somewhat complicated. Insects such as fruit flies and mites are destructive, while insects such as carpenter and honey bees are beneficial because they promote pollination necessary to fruit set.

From observations, it was found that beneficial insects were most active when flowers were in bloom. So, by timing the insecticidal spray applications, it is possible to control insect pests with little or no harm to beneficial insects. Flowers of the yellow Passion fruit are normally open from noon until nightfall. Therefore, harmful insects can be controlled by spraying the vines during the morning hours.

Fruit flies sting fruit, causing them to shrivel and become misshapen. The pests can be controlled with sprays containing Malathion. The Malathion mixture may include yeast hydrolysate as a bait spray for more effective control.

The spray should be applied to both vines and surrounding shrubbery, which may be roosting places for the flies. Sanitation practices, including removal of rotting fruit and other decaying material, will help eliminate insect pests. The spray may be applied twice a week, or until there is a reduction in the fly population.

Mite damage causes leaves to curl up and shrivel and, in severe cases, defoliation and dropping of immature fruit. A spray containing one pound of wettable sulphur in 12 gallons, or 2 tablespoons per gallon of water, will give some relief.

Plants that are growing vigorously are seldom bothered by pests. It is, therefore, important that cultural practices promoting this condition, such as proper fertilization, watering, etc. be followed.

Among the most destructive of the fungus diseases is Brown spot. Since the disease spreads fastest under humid conditions, it is most often found in wet areas. The disease causes spots to form on fruit and leaves to fall. Control it with sprays containing Maneb. Spray every two weeks until the condition has been corrected.

In harvesting, it is imperative that only ripe fruit be picked. Since it loses weight rapidly once it falls to the ground, the fruit should be picked regularly. In areas of high rainfall, fruit may rot if it is left on the ground for any length of time. Partially ripe fruit should never be harvested from the vine; even if allowed to ripen later, it will have an off-flavor.

PLUMERIA

The Plumeria, one of the most common sources of flowers for stringing into leis in Hawaii, is a native of tropical America. It belongs to the Periwinkle family *(Apocynaceae)*, and its name is derived from the French botanist, Plumier. In India, where it is also widely grown, the Plumeria is known as frangipane, a derivation from the French word, *frangipanier,* which means coagulated milk, descriptive of the thick, white rubbery latex.

Distinguishing characteristics include: (1) stiff, stout, fleshy forking branches with whitish latex; (2) large, shiny, elliptical, alternate leaves crowded at the apex; and (3) tubular fragrant flowers with five rounded petals borne in clusters at branch tips.

The tree has a broad crown, and is commonly grown for home landscaping. All varieties, except the Singapore *(Plumeria obtusa),* which is evergreen, shed their leaves sometime during the year.

The Plumeria is represented by three basic colors, namely red, yellow, and white. Since it is easy to hybridize, there are countless variations of these three colors. A good example of the white and yellow variety is *Plumeria acuminata*, commonly called the "graveyard type." The Singapore with evergreen foliage is the best example of the white variety. The red variety, or *Plumeria rubra*, is best exemplified by Scott Pratt or Hilo Beauty. It is of interest that all known hybrids of the Plumeria were produced naturally or by chance.

Because of the economic value of the blossoms, research is being conducted by the University of Hawaii to hybridize Plumeria with more attractive, longer lasting blossoms. The scientific studies also include creation of new evergreen varieties similar to the Singapore.

Plumeria makes a handsome shade tree that is especially lovely because of its sweet-scented blossoms. It grows best in open, sunny locations where it attains a height of 20 feet or more. It is quite hardy and will thrive in both arid and moist locations provided it is not waterlogged.

PROPAGATION

Plumeria may be propagated successfully by following any one of several methods. For a limited number, as for example one or two specimens for home grounds planting, it is possible to grow a plant from as large a branch as is obtainable. A branch six or more feet long may be planted directly in place and in time will root and grow. The cut end should first be allowed to stop bleeding and heal before the branch is planted. Remove leaves and insert the lower end into a prepared hole at least 12 inches deep. The hole may be drilled with a soil augur and just large enough to accommodate the branch. One advantage of this method is that the branch will remain upright with little or no support from stakes.

For situations where a large number of plants are desired, use cuttings of any size obtainable, ranging from 12 inches and over. As soon as the ends have stopped bleeding, remove leaves and plant in gallon tins with drainage holes in the bottom. Use a media of equal parts top soil and small gravel. Water and place in an out-of-the-way area. Provide moisture only when soil is dry and continue this practice even when growth begins. When plants have developed several leaves, they may be transplanted.

Plants may also be easily propagated from seeds that are encased in long, dark, paired pods. Split the pods open and gather the winged seeds for planting. Seeds may be planted in a germination flat containing equal parts of clean top soil, sand and compost. Cover seeds about 1/4 inch and water. Place flat in a sunny location and, in a few days, young seedlings will emerge from the soil.

Irrigate with water containing a small amount of dissolved fertilizer to help hasten growth. When seedlings have about four or five leaves, they are ready for lifting and transplanting into individual paper or peat pots. Transplant into a growing medium of equal parts top soil, vermiculite and humus fortified with a small amount of general garden fertilizer.

Give young transplants a thorough soaking and let stand in partial shade for a few days. They may then be exposed to full sun and allowed to grow until roots begin to penetrate through the pots. At this stage, they may be transplanted to larger containers or to wherever they are to grow.

Although it is a technique not commonly used, grafting may be undertaken producing plants sporting different shades of flowers. This is best accomplished by using a wedge or v-type of graft.

Secure a branch of the desired variety and slice the bottom into a wedge that will fit into a v-cut on a branch of the mother plant. It is important that both branches be of approximately the same size. Secure the union tightly with masking tape to be sure that it is waterproof. The operation may be repeated on as many branches as is practical. In a few weeks, the union will heal and the branch begin to grow. The tape may then be removed.

TRANSPLANTING LARGE TREES

Large, established specimens that have outgrown their original location may be transplanted with comparative ease, so long as some roots are attached. The tree may be dug up whole for transplanting elsewhere. Unless the operation is done very carelessly, chances for success are good.

Transplant the tree into a hole prepared before time. Support or prop up the tree with stakes or wire anchored to the ground. If wire is used, be sure to use sections of old garden hose to protect the trees from being cut by the wire. Give the tree a good soaking and do not water again until the soil is dry. When the tree has grown a sufficiently strong root system, the stakes and wires may be removed.

An established tree may need pruning occasionally to retain the desired shape. Make the cuts close to the union. Otherwise, Plumeria needs little or no attention except for watering and fertilizing at infrequent intervals. Plumeria is remarkably hardy and withstands neglect and very poorly-drained soils.

Gardeners interested in getting a good supply of flowers may grow Plumeria in orchard fashion. When planted in this manner, they should be spaced at least 10 to 12 feet apart to allow room for top growth.

An excellent way by which Plumeria may be grown without crowding is to grow them at the property boundary line. Grown in this manner, they provide privacy, and also serve as a windbreak. The Singapore variety is excellent for this purpose as it is never without leaves at any time of the year. Fallen leaves are excellent for compost material since they decompose readily.

POINSETTIA

Widely recognized as a symbol of the Christmas season, the Poinsettia *(Euphorbia pulcherrima)* was named for Joel R. Poinsett of South Carolina, who discovered it in its native Mexico in 1828 when he was the first American minister there.

The Poinsettia can grow into a large, shapely bush that produces very handsome heads of red, pink, or creamy white bracts. The bracts of double forms are much more numerous than in the single or ordinary kinds, and, therefore, remain attractive much longer. The bracts are modified leaves that provide the colored parts of the plant. The true flowers are the inconspicuous spherical parts in the center of the bracts cluster.

Named varieties with more attractive bracts have been developed through hybridizing by Paul Ecke of Encinitas, California. Specimens of the better varieties, some of which are patented, were donated by Ecke in 1961 to Foster Botanical Garden. Among the most outstanding is Ecke's Flaming Sphere, a mutation of another double-bracted variety. It is very ornamental and quite different from the others because the rich, blood-red bracts grow into a ball-like cluster with no horizontal bracts. Bract clusters of another variety, Barbara Ecke Supreme, measure nearly two feet across when grown under ideal conditions.

Although parts of the plant are used as medicine by Mexicans and Indians, the Poinsettia is poisonous and should be handled with caution.

POTTED PLANTS

Here are some tips to remember when buying the potted kinds from the local nurseryman. Select only plants that have good green foliage all the way down to the soil line. This is an indication that the plant is free from disease and has been cared for and fertilized properly during its growth. Examine the root system to be sure that it is strong and active and will continue to function properly. Otherwise, the plant may be weak and not be useful for very long.

Select only Poinsettias that have small green buttons in the middle of the red bracts. The green buttons indicate that the plant still has a lot of useful life left. These buttons will eventually develop into flowers that will send pollen and nectar.

PROPAGATION

Poinsettia may be grown as hedge, specimen or potted plants. They are quite handsome with their dark green foliage even when not in bloom. Poinsettia may be readily propagated from woody cuttings of old plants, or from branches pruned from potted specimens. This is the most popular method for multiplying plants. After cuttings have been divided into 9-inch sections, allow cut ends to heal or dry before planting. For containers of about gallon size, place three cuttings, each imbedded about five inches deep. Cuttings should be spaced about nine inches apart in single rows for outdoor planting. For a thick hedge, plant in double rows.

Poinsettia are remarkably hardy, and will thrive under varying conditions. However, they succeed best in full sun in loose, well-drained soil that is fertile. They will also grow in partial shade but plants will be leggy. Pests are seldom a problem. A good combination insecticide spray will give good control.

Keep cuttings moist but not waterlogged until shoots appear. When vigorous growth has begun, apply a small amount of fertilizer with the irrigation to promote rapid growth. Thereafter, keep plants watered and do not allow to go dry; otherwise, foliage will drop.

If sufficient growth has occurred by August, and low compact potted plants are desired for the holiday season, prune back to within a couple of inches of rim of container. Follow with a medium application of a complete fertilizer with the irrigation water. Depending on the wishes of the grower and how they are to be used, established plants should be trimmed or pruned back twice a year - once in March and again in August.

If potted plants are still too tall for Christmas, branches may be shortened by bending and tying them back with green plastic strips. Do this about four weeks before the holidays, so branches will have time to heal and look natural. Young branches are pliable and will respond to training. So long as branches are not completely severed from bending, they will heal and continue to grow.

A recent development in the production of highly desireable dwarf, compact potted plants is the use of chemical plant growth inhibitors or regulators. Among the most successful of several commercial preparations tried locally is Cycocel. The material diluted with water should be applied as a drench about four weeks after final pruning. The treatment reduces the length of plant internodes and slightly increases the number of bracts produced. It also causes plants to be somewhat resistant to drought.

Since Poinsettia bloom only during periods of short days, anything that interferes with this condition could prevent plants from flowering. For instance, plants growing near street lights are known to have failed to bloom. Potted specimens will last longer in the home if they are placed near a sunny location. They will also remain in better condition if they are rotated with outdoor specimens every couple or three days. Plants should be watered thoroughly before they are brought indoors to minimize the bother and necessity for watering them in the house. Unsightly pots may be concealed with foil or wrapping paper.

CUT POINSETTIA

Cut Poinsettia make nice, distinctive floral arrangements. However, because of the comparatively short span of life after cutting, they are not generally used as such. Here are suggestions for prolonging the life of cut Poinsettia:

Condition plants a week or 10 days before cutting by giving them lots of water. Since leaves do not last as long as the flowers, remove all foliage a few days before cutting. Cure cut flowers by dipping stem ends in rubbing alcohol for 10 minutes or longer. The blooms may be further hardened by immersing them in cold water for at least 30 minutes, or overnight. An alternate method is to place cut flowers treated with alcohol in plastic bags in a refrigerator for at least 24 hours.

Another conditioning technique that is quite satisfactory is to dip stem ends in boiling water or singe them over a flame for a few seconds before submerging them in ice water. Bleeding, or flow of milky sap, caused accidentally after treatment can be stopped by rubbing with clear nail polish or alcohol. Properly conditioned cut Poinsettia blossom arrangements can last from 7 to 10 days. An occasional immersion in cold water will also prolong their life.

SHOWER TREE

The Shower trees, commonly grown in Hawaii as street trees and for home grounds landscaping, belong to the Senna *(Caesalpiniodeae)* sub-family of the Bean family *(Leguminosae)*. They are related to the Cassia genus that includes some 400 species that are natives of tropical and warm regions of the world. Hardy evergreens, they have characteristic handsome foliage and abundance of long-lived, attractive blossoms with colorings of tropical brilliance.

The Golden Shower *(Cassia fistula)* comes from India and is a spreading tree about 35 feet in height with smooth, grey bark. Its large, yellow flowers hang in clusters that sometimes nearly cover the tree. The golden yellow blossoms have five conspicuously-veined petals of near-identical shape and form. The long curving pistil and stamens emerge from the center of the blossom. Seed pods, which take about a year to develop are about 1 to 2 feet long, cylindrical, and contain many yellow-brown seeds, sometimes used for leis. The compound leaves are nearly a foot long with four to eight leaflets, each about two inches long.

The Golden Shower tree is messy, especially close to and after the blossoming period, when it sheds its foliage and flowers. However, the fact that it is the only species among the four Shower trees that produces bright yellow blossoms may be sufficient reason to influence gardeners to grow it despite this fault. It requires pruning to help enhance its appearance, particularly during the time it is not in bloom.

The Coral Shower *(Cassia grandis)*, as its specific name suggests, is the largest of the Shower trees and attains a height of some 40 feet.

It is round-headed and is among the earliest Shower trees to bloom. It begins flowering shortly after the second quarter of the year when it is covered with masses of coral-pink blossoms. After the first pinkish-lavender flower buds emerge, there appears new foliage growth that is pinkish in color. Native to tropical America, it has been cultivated in the Islands since 1870.

Pinnate leaves, with at least eight pairs of large leaflets, are carried on wide spreading branches from a large trunk with smooth gray bark. Large black seed pods, more than a foot long, mature in about a year and contain yellowish seeds with foul smelling pulp. The flat, rounded seeds, about 1/2 inch long, are sometimes strung into leis.

The Pink-and-White-Shower *(Cassica javanica)*, sometimes confused with the Coral Shower, is a late bloomer and at its flowering magnificence in June. A comparatively small tree, it is a native of Sumatra and Java. Flowers borne in tight masses on the main branches are pale pink or white with yellow stamens and a green style. The foot long leaves are divided into five or more pairs of blunt, oval leaflets. Seed pods are large, black and cylindrical, and contain reddish-brown seeds that may be strung into leis.

Reputed as the most beautiful of the shower trees is the Rainbow Shower *(Cassia hybrida) (Cassia javanica x Cassia fistula)*. It is a seed-grown hybrid created by pollinating the flower of a pink-and-white Shower with that of a Golden Shower. It is, generally speaking, more floriferous and more attractive than either of its parents. No two hybrid trees are alike. All are different from each other, and flowers usually range in hue from cream or peach to orange and red. Some are golden yellow, others a rich orange-pink, and still others showing two colors because of the shade of the buds.

Foliage and flowers are intermediate in form and size, but the tree may be larger than either parent. It produces very few seed pods, and is not as messy as the other three Shower trees. It requires only light pruning to keep it looking neat.

PROPAGATION

Shower trees may be propagated from seed, cuttings or airlayers. Propagating plants from a particular specimen like a Rainbow Shower, with especially attractive blossoms, can only be done by air-layering. Select a branch that is easy to work and within easy reach. Branches that are no more than an inch in diameter are best, although it is possible to layer larger limbs.

HYBRIDIZE YOUR OWN TREE

The enterprising gardener can derive a novel sense of satisfaction and accomplishment by creating his own particular hybrid of shower tree. This can be carried out by pollinating the blossom of a selected Pink-and-White Shower with the flower from a choice Golden Shower. The pollinated flower should be bagged to prevent contamination and tagged for identification. The bag may be removed when the seed pod has formed.

Allow the seed pod to ripen to full maturity before picking. Break open the seed pod and separate seeds from the pulp. Plant seeds in a germination flat of equal parts vermiculite and clean top soil. Cover seeds with 1/4 inch of soil and moisten thoroughly. Leave the flat in the open and keep moist until seeds germinate.

After seedlings have developed a couple of pairs of true leaves, they may be irrigated with water containing a small amount of general garden fertilizer. When seedlings are about five or six inches high, they may be transplanted to convenient containers such as individual paper or peat pots.

Lift seedlings carefully from the flat and transplant to individual pots containing special media. Remove lower leaves, water thoroughly and leave transplants in the shade until they have recovered from the shock. They may then be taken out in the open and watered regularly. Fertilize weekly with soluble plant nutrients mixed with the irrigation water. When roots begin to show through the peat pots, they are ready for transplanting.

Shower trees, when planted in the right place, are handsome, showy and provide excellent shade. Carefully select the area in which they are to be planted. They require much room and, since they spread out, should not be crowded. They do best in open sun in warm lowlands.

Prepare a hole at least 15 inches wide at the top and 15 inches deep. If soil is poor, replace it with a mixture of equal parts loose top soil and humus fortified with a small amount of general garden fertilizer. A specimen growing in a peat pot may be planted as is in the middle of the hole. A plant growing in a can should be watered to ease removal. Tap the can on the sides and the plant should slip easily from the container.

The tree should receive a general garden fertilizer either with the irrigation water, or cultivated into the surface inch of soil at least twice a year until it is fully grown. Young trees need careful pruning so that they will grow into the desired shape and provide the best shade. Any young side shoots that interfere with the appearance of the main branches should be removed. The main branches should have clean lines with no distracting lower branches.

TI

Ti *(Cordyline terminalis)* is a shrubby plant with leaf clusters arranged in close spirals at branch tips. The large smooth leaves are shiny with long petioles. Foliage may be green colored or variegated. The green species introduced to Hawaii by the Polynesians is the most widely grown type in the islands. Since it very rarely produces seeds, it is propagated largely by stem cuttings. The recognized horticultural varieties were developed out of introductions from Trinidad, Tahiti and Jamaica, sometime between 1920 and 1930.

Commonly found in tropical Asia, Australia and Hawaii, Ti is a plant of many uses. It may be used for hedge or specimen planting in the home grounds, or grown in containers for display as potted or dish garden plants. In olden times, the early Hawaiians used Ti for plates and wrappers for food, house thatching, raincoats, sandals and hula skirts. It also has some value as a livestock feed. The main or tap root is thick, white and sweet. Large specimens may weigh as much as several hundred pounds. The root may be used as food or processed into confection and fermented into a drink, called Okolehau.

Leaves of the green species are used in arrangements by florists, and for Hawaiian cookery such as Kalua and Laulau. Foliage of hybrids is colorful and showy, and plants, therefore, have considerable value in home and ground beautification.

PROPAGATION

Most popular methods of propagating Ti are by cuttings, air-layering or seeds. Best cuttings for propagation are woody and may be secured close to the growing tip or close to the ground. However, young cuttings are much easier to root than those from very old wood. Cuttings may be of any length - a couple of inches or longer. For best results, the lower end of the cutting should be dipped in a hormone or rooting compound before placement in the propagation box.

The media in the rooting box may be clean soil, black sand, compost or a combination of these materials. Commercial media such as vermiculite or sponge rock also may be used. Keep the media moist in a warm spot in partial shade. Shoots will form in a couple of weeks, and after a strong root system has developed, the cuttings may be transplanted to other containers or their permanent location.

Cuttings imbedded in an upright or vertical position will grow into single plants. Cuttings planted in a reclining or horizontal position may grow into several plants, depending on their length. When shoots are large with indications of strong roots, the cuttings may be dug up and divided into as many sections as there are shoots with roots. The new cuttings may then be repotted and nursed until they are strong enough for transplanting.

Cuttings also may be rooted in plain water and should be at least six inches long. The butt end of the cuttings should be immersed in water for about an inch. Water in the container must be changed occasionally to prevent the formation of rot organisms. After a strong root system has developed, the cutting may be transplanted.

When propagating Ti by air-layering, select a strong plant and remove a 3/4 inch ring of bark. This may be 9 or 10 inches or farther from the growing point. The closer it is to the growing point, the sooner it will be possible to separate it from the mother plant. One advantage of air-layering long sections is the saving in growing time. Be sure to scrape off all bark down to the woody section. Wrap a wad of moist sphagnum moss encased in plastic wrapping around the section. Secure both ends of the plastic wrapping around the section with strong twine. When a strong root system has developed, which will be visible through plastic, the layered plant may be severed off. Carefully remove the wrapping to be sure that the roots are not damaged and transplant to a convenient container. The new plant should be nursed along until it shows signs of new growth, after which it may be transplanted.

TI FROM SEEDS

Ti may also be propagated from seeds, and these may be those of planned hybrids or crosses. Plants grown from seed may develop into choice specimens. Seeds are encased in berries about 1/4 inch in diameter. The berries should be allowed to mature to be sure that seeds are ripe before being gathered. The berries may be planted whole in seedling boxes. However, to hasten germination, the berries may be mashed to release the seeds before planting.

For germinating seeds, use a fine media such as screened fern fiber, sand, or some commercial media. Cover the seeds about 1/4 inch deep and keep moist in a warm spot. The young seedlings look like fine blades of grass in the early stages. To hasten growth, they should receive water that has been fortified with a small amount of a complete fertilizer. When they are several inches high, or have developed strong roots, they should be transferred to individual pots or containers. They may be left in the containers until they are ready for transplanting elsewhere.

WHERE TO GROW

Ti will grow in most types of island soils that have good drainage. They like a lot of moisture and will grow only as well as the amount of water they receive. Some varieties will grow in full sun, while others require partial shade, such as a tree, that allows light to filter through. They may also be grown in containers and placed or moved about in areas of best light conditions.

For growing out in the open, dig the planting hole at least six inches wide and some 10 inches deep. If the soil is poor and tight, replace with loose top soil incorporated with much organic matter, to which has been added a small amount of a general garden fertilizer.

The plant may be planted deep without adverse effect, but a good practice is to have about two or three inches of soil above the root zone. After the plant is in place, follow with a generous amount of water. Besides regular watering, it will need occasional applications of a general garden fertilizer at three or four month intervals.

Potted plants will succeed best in a media consisting of fertile top soil mixed with lots of humus plus a small amount of black sand. Apply a small amount of fertilizer with the irrigation water once each month.

PESTS

For best display, Ti must be mature with undamaged foliage. Since leaves are somewhat tender, they are easily damaged by insects. Most common insect pests are aphids, scales and grasshoppers. These feed on foliage causing an unsightly appearance. For control, use an insecticide such as Malathion.

To control snails and slugs use a commercial bait containing metaldehyde.

Fuasarium, a fungus disease, often attacks the growing tips, causing die-back to the cane. This is most common in areas of high rainfall. A fungicide spray containing zinc will offer some relief.

TREE FERN

The Tree Fern *(Cibotium chamisssoi)*, also known in Hawaiian as hapu'u pulu, is native to and one of the commonest of its kind in Hawaii. It is a member of the Dicksonia family *(Dicksoniaceae)*, one of some 20 families of Ferns. It is a large flowerless perennial with huge leaves covered with fruiting bodies at the edge of the under side of the fronds.

In the rain forests of the Big Island, there are huge specimens whose age is a mystery. However, these descendants of a prehistoric type of vegetation are far older than generally believed. The age of the standing plant is difficult to estimate. The average rate of growth of relatively young Tree Ferns is about 3 1/2 inches per year. However, this increase in height decreases progressively as the growing area is elevated from the ground.

The frond stems of the hapu'u pulu are brown and smooth, and differ from that of another native Hawaiian Tree Fern known as hapu'u i'i, which sports a thick growth of stiff blackish hair on front stems. The hapu'u i'i is also somewhat larger and has more leathery frond stems. Otherwise, both varieties are almost identical in appearance.

At the growing point, the young fronds are covered with a fawn-colored material formerly used as stuffing for pillows and mattresses when dried. Newly opened fronds are mealy and used as livestock feed. Orientals cut them in sections and boil them for hours until most of the bitter black liquid has been removed. These are then sliced into strips, kept in water and sold as a vegetable. They have a distinctive flavor, and are excellent when cooked with beef, pork or chicken.

Hapu'u, whether live or dead, is commonly used by local gardeners. In wet areas, where it is at home, hapu'u is popular for home grounds landscaping. It may also be grown in dry locations, but requires copious irrigation to keep it alive. The need for frequent watering in dry locations can be minimized by planting hapu'u in groups of three. Grown in this manner, moisture evaporation is somewhat lessened. A good landscaping trick is to plant specimens of different heights in the same group.

KEEP THEM WET

In planting hapu'u, the soil does not need to be well-cultivated. Dig a hole just large enough to accommodate the plants. The opening should be at least 12 inches deep. Drop the plants in the hole and brace them upright with stones in the bottom before covering with soil. Tamp the surface well and remove any open fronds that may still be attached to the plants. Follow this with a good soaking, making sure to wet the trunk and ground thoroughly.

New plants have to be kept moist; otherwise, they may die. When the young fronds begin to open, suggesting that the plants are growing, less moisture may be applied. However, in no case should they be allowed to dry completely. This may result in premature drying of the fronds. Since only plants with live foliage present the best appearance, any fronds or sections of fronds that have dried should be removed. During windy weather plants should be watered more often; otherwise, fronds will dry up in time.

Hapu'u are sometimes planted as a garden screen or property fence. When grown as a screen, plants preferably of different heights should be grouped in a line. However, when used as a fence, it is more desirable to use plants of identical height. They may then need special bracing, as an unusually strong gust of wind may topple them over. When they have grown strong roots, the braces may be removed.

The shade cast by hapu'u fronds is near ideal for anthurium cultivation. Therefore, many gardeners grow anthuriums either potted or directly in the ground close to hapu'u plantings. Besides, the group planting makes an attractive addition to the landscaping.

Although hapu'u very seldom branches, occasionally there grows a specimen that may produce a side shoot. Such a plant lends interest because of its novelty.

MANY USES

The trunk of the hapu'u is useful for attaching certain types of orchids. It may be used for direct attachment of certain dendrobiums, and specimens grown in containers may be hung on the trunk.

Live hapu'u may be grown in containers for indoor display, but since hapu'u are outdoor plants, they cannot be left indoors for any length of time. If they are to be used with any regularity in this manner, there should be several potted specimens for frequent change.

The many uses for dead or dried hapu'u in local gardening are widely recognized. When sawed into sections or split in half, they are ideal for the culture of certain types of orchids such as dendrobiums. Holes may be drilled with an augur and the young orchids inserted in them. The orchids are nursed at first, and eventually grow into large specimens with roots firmly attached to the log.

Orchid growers, wanting to use all available garden space, sometimes mount split hapu'u logs on top of wooden or rock fences. These logs are used to grow sun-loving orchids like Renatheras, Dendrobiums and others.

Small chunks of hapu'u, when placed in containers, appear to be the ideal media for strap-leafed Vandas and other orchids. These are also useful for lining wire baskets for plants. They decompose rather slowly, and take a long while before they have to be replaced. Hapu'u dust, like that resulting from sawing logs, may be used by itself or mixed with other material to form an excellent media for growing young orchids or other seedling plants.

Large logs are also fashioned into fern pots, which are not only novel but also useful as containers for plants. These are also carved into garden ornaments such as tikis.

Perhaps the greatest use for hapu'u is as shredded fiber for a potting media. When the material is mixed in quantity with tight soil, drainage is improved. Orchid growers found out long ago that their plants seemed to thrive when grown in hapu'u fiber. The material is tough enough so that it does not break down as rapidly as other orchid growing media. This means a substantial savings in time that otherwise would be devoted to repotting. Besides, in comparison with materials such as sphagnum and others, hapu'u fiber is rather inexpensive. However, because it contains little or no nutrient, plants grown in it need to be fertilized regularly; otherwise, they will suffer.